A
SOUND
of Thunder

A Sound of Thunder
© 1993, Addison-Wesley Publishers Limited and Rubicon Publishing Inc.

ISBN 0-201-60217-2
Canadian Cataloguing in Publication Data
Main entry under title:

A Sound of thunder: a green anthology

Includes bibliographical references.
ISBN 0-201-60217-2

1. Ecology - Literary collections 2. Man -influence
on nature - Literary collections 3. Environmental protection - Literary collections I. Mills,
Ian W. (Ian William), 1943 –

PN6071. H78S68 1993   808.8'0355   C92-094793 – X

Cover art: "The Choir of Sphinxes," 1964, by René Magritte.
©1993 C. Herscovici/ ARS, New York.

Cover Design: *Wycliffe Smith*
Text Design: *Claudia Neri, Wycliffe Smith Design Inc.*
Editors: *Mei-lin Cheung, Elizabeth Siegel Masih*
Editorial Assistant: *Shen-Yi Goh*

**The Publishers gratefully acknowledge the following educators for
their insightful reviews and suggestions:**

Lynn Archer, Surrey School District, British Columbia
Bil Chinn, Edmonton Public Schools, Alberta
Nolan Taggert, The Durham Board of Education, Oshawa, Ontario
Barbara Cole, Peel Board of Education, Ontario
Peter Fanning, Vancouver Board of Education, British Columbia

93 94 95 96 97   5 4 3 2 1

SOUND
of Thunder

**Edited by
Ian Mills**

The frog does not drink up
the pond in which he lives.
Indian Proverb

From Nature's chain, whatever link you strike,
Tenth, or ten thousandth, breaks the chain alike.
Alexander Pope

Addison-Wesley Publishers Limited
Rubicon Publishing Inc.

Table of

The House Of Life

Unintended Consequences

Contents

JUST ONE THING

INTRODUCTION

Just as a rumble of thunder in the distance presages a storm, so many authors have sounded warnings about the world and the environment in their writings; for years, writers have sought to alert their readers to an approaching storm of environmental problems and perhaps even disasters.

The aim of this collection of writings on the environment is not simply to inform and entertain but also to stimulate inquiry and action. Ray Bradbury's "A Sound of Thunder" explores cause and effect in the framework of a time travel dinosaur hunt adventure story; Doris Lessing's "A Sunrise On The Veld" shows "nature red on tooth and claw;" while in "The Thrill Of The Grass," W. P. Kinsella whimsically scores one for the natural approach.

This book does not attempt to be topical. In a world and an area that change so rapidly, today's topicality becomes tomorrow's history. The preponderance of poetry and fiction is deliberate, since informative articles on air, land, and water pollution, waste management, and species extinction can be found almost daily in any number of magazines or newspapers; television also provides plenty of information and statistics in these areas. Topical nonfiction suffers most from the passage of time and consequently, the non-fiction selections here have been chosen for their "timeless" quality in that their considerations are not limited to a specific time and place but attempt to move beyond the particular to reach a perception that is valid in a broader context. Some poems and stories in this collection were written more than thirty years ago and yet the writers' concerns are often more relevant today than when the pieces were first published; with thousands of species made extinct each year the message of "A Sound of Thunder" or of "Before Eden" begs to be heard and not to be ignored for another thirty years.

The problems with the environment are a global concern. Hence the voices in this collection of fiction, nonfiction, and poetry, come from around the world — from Canada and the USA, from Chile and Sri Lanka, from the UK and South Africa.

The sections in this anthology attempt to reflect the progression in humanity's relationship with the natural world. The selections in the first unit, "The House of Life," show the natural world in balance — sometimes beautiful, sometimes unpleasant, sometimes serene, sometimes violent — and always interconnected.

Humans have long recognized the healing power of nature, the peace of wild places, and the more than physical craving for clean water and space, all of which are no more than a recognition of the human need to be in harmony with the natural world. In times past humans could rationally conceive of the world as infinite, but decades of pictures from a different perspective have shown the world to be, in reality, no more than a "big blue marble" and from that image of finiteness it is only a small mental step for humankind to see the globe as the house of life. If Earth is the house of life, then all that lives is one extended family. The selections in this unit celebrate life and humanity and their mutuality.

Just as people tinker with their house so do they tinker with the environment, but there is a limit to the interference that nature can tolerate and many feel that the limit has been passed. Consequences, intended and otherwise, follow. The pieces in the unit "Unintended Consequences" highlight the problems that arise from human carelessness and callousness with regard to the environment and warn of the possible consequences of continued irresponsibility.

Ultimately, matters must be set right and while it may require a concerted effort to undo the harm, the writers in the final unit, "Just One Thing," suggest that one positive act can have a significant impact on the world and that disaster should inspire actions and not despair.

This book is for any reader, but it is primarily for the young, for it is they who will inherit the world. If any of the literature teaches, the reader gains; if it prompts to action, then the world gains.

Ian Mills

Who Am I?

FELICE HOLMAN

The trees ask me,
And the sky,
And the sea asks me
        Who am I?

The grass asks me,
And the sand,
And the rocks ask me
        Who am I?

The wind tells me
At nightfall,
And the rain tells me
    Someone small.

        Someone small
        Someone small
            But a piece
                    of
                    it
                    all.

THE LAWS of Nature

T.C. McLuhan

Okute, or Shooter, an old Teton Sioux, in speaking in 1911 about his holy beliefs, explains that his people believed in a mysterious power whose greatest manifestation was nature, one representation of which was the sun. Adds Redbird, a member of the same tribe, "we made sacrifices to the sun, and our petitions were granted."

All living creatures and all plants derive their life from the sun. If it were not for the sun, there would be darkness and nothing could grow — the earth would be without life. Yet the sun must have the help of the earth. If the sun alone were to act upon animals and plants, the heat would be so great that they would die, but there are clouds that bring rain, and the action of the sun and earth together supply the moisture they find. This is according to the laws of nature and is one of the evidences of the wisdom of Wakan tanka. Plants are sent by Wakan tanka and come from the ground at his command, the part to be affected by the sun and rain appearing above the ground and the roots pressing downward to find the moisture which is supplied for them. Animals and plants are taught by Wakan tanka what they are to do. Wakan tanka teaches the birds to make nests, yet the nests of all birds are not alike. Wakan tanka gives them merely the outline. Some make better nests than others. In the same way some animals are satisfied with very rough dwellings, while others make attractive places in which to live. Some animals also take better care of their young than others. The forest is the home of many birds and other animals, and the water is the home of fish and reptiles. All birds, even those of the same species, are not alike, and it is the same with animals and with human beings. The reason Wakan tanka does not make two birds, or animals, or human beings exactly alike is because each is placed here by Wakan tanka to be an independent individual and to rely on itself. Some animals are made to live in the ground. The stones and the minerals are placed in the ground by Wakan tanka, some stones being more exposed than others. When a medicine man says that he talks with the sacred stones, it is because of all the substance in the ground these are the ones which most often appear in dreams and are able to communicate with men.

From my boyhood I have observed leaves, trees, and grass, and I have never found two alike. They may have a general likeness, but on examination I have found that they differ slightly. Plants are of different families....It is the same with animals....It is the same with human beings; there is some place which is best adapted to each. The seeds of the plants are blown about by the wind until they reach the place where they will grow best — where the action of the sun and the presence of moisture are most favourable to them, and there they take root and grow. All living creatures and all plants are a benefit to something. Certain animals fulfill their purpose by definite acts. The crows, buzzards and flies are somewhat similar in their use, and even the snakes have purpose in being. In the early days the animals probably roamed over a very wide country until they found a proper place. An animal depends a great deal on the natural conditions around it. If the buffalo were here today, I think they would be different from the buffalo of the old days because all the natural conditions have changed. They would not find the same food, nor the same surroundings. We see the change in our ponies. In the old days they could stand great hardship and travel long distance without water. They lived on certain kinds of food and drank pure water. Now our horses require a mixture of food; they have less endurance and must have constant care. It is the same with Indians; they have less freedom and they fall an easy prey to disease. In the old days they were rugged and healthy, drinking pure water and eating the meat of the buffalo which had a wide range, not being shut up like cattle of the present day. The water of the Missouri River is not pure, as it used to be, and many of the creeks are no longer good for us to drink.

A man ought to desire that which is genuine instead of that

which is artificial. Long ago there was no such thing as a mixture of earths to make paint. There were only three colours of native earth paint — red, white, and black. These could be obtained only in certain places. When other colours were desired, the Indians mixed the juices of plants, but it was found that these mixed colours faded and it could always be told when the red was genuine, the red made of burned clay.

AUTOBIOGRAPHY of
a Lungworm

ROY FULLER

My normal dwelling is the lungs of swine,
    my normal shape a worm,
But other dwellings, other shapes, are mine
    Within my natural term.
Dimly I see my life, of all, the sign,
    Of better lives the germ.

The pig, though I am inoffensive, coughs,
    Finding me irritant:
My eggs go with the contents of the troughs
    From mouth to excrement —
The pig thus thinks, perhaps, he forever doffs
    His niggling resident.
The eggs lie unconsidered in the dung
    Upon the farmyard floor,
Far from the scarlet and sustaining lung:
    But happily a poor
And humble denizen provides a rung
    To make ascension sure.

The earthworm eats the eggs; inside the warm
    Cylinder larvae hatch:
For years, if necessary, in this form
    I wait the lucky match
That will return me to my cherished norm,
    My ugly pelt dispatch.

ROY FULLER   Strangely, it is the pig himself becomes
    The god inside the car:
His greed devours the earthworms; so the slums
    Of his intestines are
The setting for the act when clay succumbs
    And force steers for its star.

The larvae burrow through the bowel wall
    And, having to the dregs
Drained ignominy, gain the lung's great hall.
    They change. Once more, like pegs,
Lungworms are anchored to the rise and fall
    — And start to lay their eggs.

What does this mean? The individual,
    Nature, mutation, strife?
I feel, though I am simple, still the whole
    Is complex; and that life —
A huge, doomed throbbing — has a wiry soul
    That must escape the knife.

THE BIRD

AND THE SNAKE

LOREN EISELEY

"The special value of science," a perceptive philosopher once wrote, "lies not in what it makes of the world, but in what it makes of the knower." Some years ago, while camping in a vast eroded area in the West, I came upon one of those unlikely sights which illuminate such truths.

I suppose that nothing living had moved among those great stones for centuries. They lay toppled against each other like fallen dolmens. The huge stones were beast, I used to think, of a kind man ordinarily lived too fast to understand. They seemed inanimate because the tempo of the life in them was slow. They lived ages in one place and moved only when man was not looking. Sometimes at night I would hear a low rumble as one drew itself into a new position and subsided again. Sometimes I found their tracks ground deeply into the hillsides.

It was with considerable surprise that while traversing this barren valley, I came, one afternoon, upon what I can only describe as a very remarkable sight. Some distance away, so far that for a little space I could make nothing of the spectacle, my eyes were attracted by a dun-coloured object about the size of a football, which periodically bounded up from the desert floor. Wonderingly, I drew closer and observed that something ropelike which glittered in the sun appeared to be dangling from the ball-shaped object. Whatever the object was, it appeared to be bouncing faster and more desperately as I approached. My surroundings were such that this hysterical dance of what at first glance appeared to be a common stone was quite unnerving, as though suddenly all the natural objects in the valley were about to break into a jig. Going closer, I penetrated the mystery.

LOREN EISELEY   The sun was sparkling on the scales of a huge blacksnake which was partially looped about the body of a hen pheasant. Desperately the bird tried to rise, and just as desperately the big snake coiled and clung, though each time the bird, falling several feet, was pounding the snake's body in the gravel. I gazed at the scene in astonishment. Here in this silent waste, like an emanation from nowhere, two bitter and desperate vapours, two little whirl-winds of contending energy, were beating each other to death because their plans, — something, I suspected, about whether a clutch of eggs was to turn into a thing with wings or scales — this problem, I say, of the onrushing nonexistent future, had catapulted serpent against bird.

The bird was too big for the snake to have had it in mind as prey. Most probably, he had been intent on stealing the pheasant's eggs and had been set upon and pecked. Somehow in the ensuing scuffle he had flung a loop over the bird's back and partially blocked her wings. She could not take off, and the snake would not let go. The snake was taking a heavy battering among the stones, but the high-speed metabolism and tremendous flight exertion of the mother bird were rapidly exhausting her. I stood a moment and saw the bloodshot glaze deepen in her eyes. I suppose I could have waited there to see what would happen when she could not fly; I suppose it might have been worth scientifically recording. But I could not stand that ceaseless, bloody pounding in the gravel. I thought of the eggs somewhere about, and whether they were to elongate and writhe into an armour of scale, or eventually to go whistling into the wind with their wild mother.

So I, the mammal, in my way supple, and less bound by instinct, arbitrated the matter. I unwound the serpent from the bird and let him hiss and wrap his battered coils around my arm. The bird, her wings flung out, rocked on her legs and gasped repeatedly. I moved away in order not to drive her further from her nest. Thus the serpent and I, two terrible and feared beings, passed quickly out of view.

Over the next ridge, where he could do no more damage, I let the snake, whose anger had subsided, slowly uncoil and slither from my arm. He flowed away into a little patch of bunch grass — aloof, forgetting, unaware of the journey he had made upon my wrist, which throbbed from his expert constriction. The bird had contended for birds against the oncoming future; the serpent writhing into the bunch grass had contended just as desperately for serpents. And I, the apparition in that valley — for what had I contended? — I who contained the serpent and the bird and who read the past long written in their bodies.

Slowly, as I sauntered dwarfed among overhanging pinnacles, as the great slabs which were the visible remnants of past ages laid their enormous shadows rhythmically as life and death across my face, the answer came to me. Man could contain more than himself. Among these many appearances that flew, or swam in the waters, or wavered momentarily into being, man alone possessed that unique ability.

The Renaissance thinkers were right when they said that man, the Microcosm, contains the Macrocosm. I had touched the lives of creatures other than myself and had seen their shapes waver and blow like smoke through the corridors of time. I had watched, with sudden concentrated attention, myself, this brain, unrolling from the seed like a genie from a bottle, and casting my eyes forward, I had seen it vanish again into the formless alchemies of the earth.

For what then had I contended, weighing the serpent with the bird in that wild valley? I had struggled, I am now convinced, for a greater, more comprehensive version of myself.

Snake

D.H. Lawrence

A snake came to my water-trough
On a hot, hot day, and I in pyjamas for the heat,
To drink there.

In the deep, strange-scented shade of the great dark carob-
    tree
I came down the steps with my pitcher
And must wait, must stand and wait, for there he was at the
    trough before me.

He reached down from a fissure in the earth-wall in the
    gloom
And trailed his yellow-brown slackness soft-bellied down,
    over the edge of the stone trough
And rested his throat upon the stone bottom,
And where the water had dripped from the tap, in a small
    clearness,
He sipped with his straight mouth,
Softly drank through his straight gums, into his slack long
    body,
Silently.

Someone was before me at my water-trough,
And I, like a second-comer, waiting.

He lifted his head from his drinking, as cattle do,
And looked at me vaguely, as drinking cattle do,
And flickered his two-forked tongue from his lips, and
    mused a moment,
And stooped and drank a little more,
Being earth-brown, earth-golden from the burning bowels
of the earth
On the day of Sicilian July, with Etna smoking.

The voice of my education said to me
He must be killed,
For in Sicily the black, black snakes are innocent, the gold
    are venomous.

And voices in me said, If you were a man
You would take a stick and break him now, and finish him
    off.

But must I confess how I liked him,
How glad I was he had come like a guest in quiet, to drink
    at my water-trough
And depart peaceful, pacified, and thankless,
Into the burning bowels of this earth?

Was it cowardice, that I dared not kill him?
Was it perversity, that I longed to talk to him?
Was it humility, to feel honoured?
I felt so honoured.

And yet those voices:
If you were not afraid, you would kill him!

And truly I was afraid, I was most afraid,
But even so, honoured still more
That he should seek my hospitality
From out the dark door of the secret earth.

He drank enough
And lifted his head, dreamily, as one who has drunken,
And flickered his tongue like a forked night on the air, so
    black,
Seeming to lick his lips,
And looked around like a god, unseeing, into the air,
And slowly turned his head,
And slowly, very slowly, as if thrice adream,
Proceeded to draw his slow length curving round
And climb again the broken bank of my wall-face.

SNAKE

D.H. LAWRENCE   And as he put his head into that dreadful hole,
                  And as he slowly drew up, snake-easing his shoulders,
and
          entered farther,
A sort of horror, a sort of protest against his withdrawing
          into that horrid black hole,
Deliberately going into the blackness, and slowly drawing
          himself after,
Overcame me now his back was turned.

I looked round, I put down my pitcher,
I picked up a clumsy log
And threw it at the water-trough with a clatter.

I think it did not hit him,
But suddenly that part of him that was left behind
          convulsed in undignified haste,
Writhed like lightning, and was gone
Into the black hole, the earth-lipped fissure in the wall-
          front,
At which, in the intense still noon, I stared with
          fascination
And immediately I regretted it.
I thought how paltry, how vulgar, what a mean act!
I despised myself and the voices of my accursed human
          education.

And I thought of the albatross,
And I wished he would come back, my snake.

For he seemed to me again like a king,
Like a king in exile, uncrowned in the underworld,
Now due to be crowned again.

And so, I missed my chance with one of the lords
Of life.
And I have something to expiate;
A pettiness.

The Great American Forest

RUTHERFORD PLATT

Food in the human menu is hardly recognized as packaged sunlight, but that is exactly what it is. The art of packaging sunlight was originally discovered by plants in the sea, and seaweeds carried the formula for photosynthesis to the water's edge. There they delivered it to ferns and mosses, which in turn bequeathed it to trees.

Growing in the sunlight, trees could make full use of photosynthesis; in fact, their energy factory worked so well that packaged sunlight was not only incorporated into food but into wood, as we have seen. Then wood, in turn, increased the production of packaged sunlight by lifting green needles and leaves high off the ground into more winds, bringing more oxygen and giving more exposure to sunlight. These towering arrangements led to the grand climax of forests...

At first glance, a leaf may look as thin as paper; actually it is a spreading one-storey factory with ample room between floor and ceiling for sunlight-packaging machinery. The standard leaf is designed for utility to present a broad surface to the sunlight. A mature maple tree spreads several hundred thousand leaves with a surface of some two thousand square yards (about half an acre) of chlorophyll.

A square yard of leaf surface in full operation packs about a gram of carbohydrate per hour. This may seem to be a small amount; a gram weighs about as much as the common straight pin. But food production of that half acre of chlorophyll mounts with each hour of every day. There are no Sunday and holiday shutdowns. Photosynthesis does not require a bright sunny day, it works even better when the sky is overcast. Operating an average of ten hours a day during June, July and August, each square yard of maple leaf surface packs a pound and a half of carbohydrate. The seasonal production by the leaves of a single maple tree can total 3,630 pounds of packaged sunlight!

Walimai

ISABEL ALLENDE

The name given me by my father is Walimai, which in the tongue of our brothers in the north means "wind." I can tell it to you, since now you are like my own daughter and you have my permission to call my name, although only when we are among family. The names of persons and living creatures demand respect, because when we speak them we touch their heart and become part of their life force. This is how we blood kinsmen greet each other. I cannot understand the ease with which the white ones call each others' names, with no fear; not only does it show a lack of respect, it can also lead to grave danger. I have noted that these persons speak unthinkingly, not realizing that to speak is also to be. Word and gestures are man's thought. We should not speak without reason, this I have taught my sons and daughters, but they do not always listen to my counsel. Long ago, taboos and traditions were respected. My grandfathers, and the grandfathers of my grandfathers, received all necessary knowledge from their grandfathers. Nothing changed. A man with a good memory could recall every teaching he had received and thus knew what to do in any situation. But then came the white ones speaking against the wisdom of the grandfathers, and pushing us off our land. We move always deeper into the jungle, but always they overtake us, sometimes years pass, but finally they come again, and we must destroy our planted fields, put our children on our backs, bind our animals, and depart. So it has been as long as I have memory: leave everything and run away like mice — not the mighty warriors and gods who inhabited these lands in days of old. Some of our young are curious about the whites, and while we travel deeper into the forest to continue our lives as our ancestors did, others undertake a different path. We think of those who leave as if they were dead, because very few return, and those that do have changed so that we cannot recognize them as kinsmen.

They tell that in the years before I came into the world not enough women were born to our people, and thus my father had to travel long roads to seek a wife from a different tribe. He journeyed through the forests, following the marks of others who had travelled that route before him and for the same purpose and returned with women not of our blood. After much travelling, when my father had begun to lose hope of finding a life companion, he saw a girl standing by a tall waterfall, a river that fell from the sky. Staying some distance away, in order not to frighten her, he spoke to her in the tone that hunters use to calm their prey, and explained his need to marry her. She made signs that he might come near, studied him openly, and must have been pleased by the face of the traveller, because she decided that the idea of marriage was not a rash one. My father had to work for his father-in-law until he paid for the woman's value. After they had fulfilled the rituals of marriage, they made the return journey to our village.

I grew up with my brothers and sisters beneath the canopies of tall trees, never seeing the sun. Sometimes a wounded tree would fall, leaving an opening in the thick dome of the forest, at those times we saw the blue eye of the sky. My father and mother told me stories, they sang songs to me, and taught me what a man must know to survive alone, with nothing but his bow and arrows. I was free. We, the Children of the Moon, cannot live unless we are free. When we are closed inside walls or bars we collapse inward, we become blind and deaf, and in a few days our spirit detaches itself from the bones of our chest and abandons us. At those times we become like miserable beasts and, almost always, we prefer to die. That is why our houses have no walls, only a sloped roof to stop the wind and shed the rain; beneath it we hang our hammocks close together, because we like to listen to the dreams of the women and the children and feel the breath of the monkeys and dogs and pigs that sleep beneath the same shelter. In the earliest times we lived in the jungles without knowing that there was a world beyond the cliffs and rivers. Friends came to visit from other tribes, and told us rumours of Boa Vista and El Plantanal, of the white ones and their customs, but we believed these were only stories to make us laugh. I reached manhood, and my turn came to find a wife, but I decided to wait, because I liked being with the bachelors; we were happy, and

WALIMAI

ISABEL ALLENDE   lived well. Even so, I could not devote myself fully
to games and resting as the others did, because my family is very
large: my brothers and sisters, cousins, nieces and nephews, many
mouths to feed, and much work for a hunter.

One day a group of the pale men came to our village. They
hunted with powder, from far away, without skill or courage; they
could not climb a tree or spear a fish in the water, they moved clumsily through the jungle, they were always getting tangled in their
packs, their weapons, even their own feet. They did not clothe themselves in air, as we do, but wore wet and stinking clothing; they were
dirty and they did not know the laws of decency, but they insisted on
telling us of their knowledge and their gods. We compared them
with what we had been told about the white men, and we verified the
truth of that gossip. Soon we realized that these men were not mis-
sionaries, or soldiers or rubber collectors: they were mad. They
wanted the land, they wanted to carry away the wood; they were also
searching for stones. We explained that the jungle is not something
to be tossed over your shoulder and transported like a dead bird, but
they did not want to hear our arguments. They made a camp near
our village. Each one of them was like a wind of catastrophe; he
destroyed everything he touched; he left a trail of waste behind him;
he disturbed animals and people. At first we obeyed the laws of
courtesy, and pleased them, because they were our guests, but they
were never satisfied, they always wanted more, until weary of their
games, we declared war with all traditional ceremonies. They are not
good warriors, they are easily frightened and their fragile skullbones
could not withstand the clubbing we gave them. Afterward we abandoned our village and we journeyed to the east where the forest is
impenetrable, travelling for long stretches through the tops of trees
so that their companions could not find us. We had been told that
for each one of them that dies, even in fair battle, they are capable of
eliminating an entire tribe, including the children. We discovered a
place to establish a new village. It was not as good — the women
had to walk hours to find clean water — but we stayed there because
we believed that no one would come so far to search for us. A year
later I was far from our village following the tracks of a puma, when I
approached too near a camp of soldiers. I was tired, and had not
eaten in several days, for this reason, I used poor judgement. Instead

of turning back when I glimpsed the strangers, I lay down to rest. The soldiers caught me. They did not mention the men we had clubbed to death. In fact, they asked me nothing; perhaps they did not know those men or did not know that I am Walimai. They pressed me into work with the rubber collectors, with many men from other tribes, men they had dressed in trousers and driven to work with no thought for their wishes. The rubber demands much care, and there were not enough people to do the work; that was why they forced us. That was a time without freedom, and I do not want to speak of it. I stayed only to see whether I could learn anything, but from the beginning I knew I would return to my people. Nothing can long hold a warrior against his will.

We worked from sun to sun, some bleeding the trees to drain their life drop by drop, others cooking the liquid to thicken it and form it into great balls. The air outdoors was sick with the stench of the burned sap, and the air indoors in the sleeping quarters foul with the sweat of the men. No one could draw a deep breath in that place. They gave us maize to eat, and bananas, and the strange contents of some cans, which I never tasted, because nothing good for humans can grow in tins. At one end of the camp they had built a large hut where they kept the women. After two weeks of working with the raw rubber, the boss handed me a slip of paper and sent me where the women were. He also gave me a cup of liquor which I turned out on the ground because I have seen how that water destroys a man's good sense. I stood in line with the others. I was the last, and when it came to my turn to enter the hut, the sun had gone down and night begun, with its clamour of frogs and parrots.

She was of the tribe of the Ila, the people of gentle heart, from which the most delicate girls come. Some men travel months on end to find the Ila, they take them gifts and hunt for them in the hope of obtaining one of their women. She looked like a lizard lying there, but I recognized her because my mother, too, was an Ila woman. She lay naked on her straw mat, tied by one ankle to a chain staked in the ground, sluggish, as if she had breathed in the *yopo* of the acacia, she had the smell of sick dogs, and she was wet with the dew of all the men who had covered her before me. She was the size of a young boy, and her bones clicked like small stones in the river.

ISABEL ALLENDE   The Ila women remove all of their bodily hair, even their eyelashes; they adorn their ears with feathers and flowers; they thrust polished sticks through their cheeks and nose; they paint designs over all their body in the reds of the annato, the deep purple of the palm, and the black of carbon.   But she had none of that.   I placed my machete on the ground, and greeted her as a sister, imitating some songbirds and the sound of rivers.   She did not respond.   I pounded her chest, to see whether her spirit still resonated in her rib cage, but there was no echo, her soul was very weak and could not answer me.   Kneeling beside her, I gave her water to drink and spoke to her in my mother's tongue.   She opened her eyes and stared at me a long time.   I understood.

First of all, I washed myself without wasting the clean water. I took a good draft into my mouth and sprinkled it in small streams onto my hands, which I rubbed carefully and then wet to clean my face.   I did the same with her, to cleanse the men's dew from her body.   I removed the trousers the boss had given me.   From a cord at my waist hung my sticks for making fire, the tips of arrows, my roll of tobacco, my wooden knife with a rat's tooth in the point, and a bag of strong leather in which I carried a small amount of curare.   I spread a bit of that paste on the point of my knife, bent over the woman and, with the poisoned instrument, opened a small cut in her neck.   Life is a gift from the gods.   The hunter kills to feed his family; he tries not to eat the flesh of his prey but prefers to eat what another hunter offers him.   At times, tragically, a man kills another in war, but he never harms a woman or a child.   She looked at me with large eyes yellow as honey, and I thought she tried to smile, gratefully.   For her I had violated the first taboo of the Children of the Moon, and I would have to pay for my shame with many labours of expiation.   I held my ear to her mouth, and she murmured her name.   I repeated it twice in my mind to be very sure, but did not speak it aloud; it is not good to mention the dead or disturb their peace, and she was already dead even though her heart still beat. Soon I saw the muscles of her belly, her chest, her arms stiffen with paralysis; she stopped breathing, and changed colour.   A sigh escaped her, and her body died without a struggle, as small creatures die.

Immediately, I felt her spirit leave through her nostrils and enter mine, anchoring itself to my breastbone.   All her weight fell

upon me, and I had to struggle to get to my feet. I moved very slowly, as if I were under water. I arranged her body in the position of the
last rest, with her knees touching her chin. I bound her with fibers
from the mat, then made a mound with the rest of the straw and used
my sticks to make fire. When I saw that the fire was blazing intense-
ly, I left the hut slowly, labouriously climbed the camp fence —
because she kept dragging me down — and walked into the forest. I
had reached the first trees when I heard the alarm bells.

I walked all the first day without stopping. On the second
day I fashioned a bow and arrows so I could hunt for her, and for
myself as well. The warrior who bears the weight of another human
life must fast for ten days; in this way the spirit of the dead one
grows weak; finally it lets go and journeys to the land of the souls.
If the warrior does not do this, the spirit grows fat on the food it is
fed and grows inside the man until it suffocates him. I have seen
men of great courage die this way. But before I fulfilled those conditions, I had to lead the spirit of the Ila woman into the thickest
jungle where she would never be found. I ate very little, barely
enough not to kill her a second time. Each mouthful tasted like
spoiled meat, and every sip of water was bitter, but I forced myself to
swallow, to nourish the two of us. For one complete cycle of the
moon I travelled deep into the jungle, carrying inside me the soul of
the woman who weighed more each day. We spoke often. The
tongue of the Ila is uninhibited and resounds beneath the trees with a
long echo. We communicated singing, with our body, with our eyes,
our waist, our feet. I repeated to her the legends I had learned from
my mother and my father, I told her my past, and she told me of the
first part of her life, when she was a happy girl playing with her
brothers and sisters, rolling in the mud and swinging from the high
branches. Out of courtesy, she did not mention her recent past of
misfortune and and humiliation. I caught a white bird; I plucked the
finest feathers and made adornments for her ears. At night I kept a
small fire burning so she would not be cold, and so jaguars or serpents would not disturb her sleep. I bathed her in the river with
care, rubbing her with ash and crushed flowers, to take away her bad
memories.

Finally one day we reached the perfect spot, and had no further excuse to continue walking. There the jungle was so dense that

ISABEL ALLENDE   in places I had to open a path by slashing the under-growth with my machete, even my teeth, and we had to speak in a low voice not to alter the silence of time. I chose a place near a thread of water, I put up a roof of leaves and made a hammock for her from three long strips of bark. With my knife I shaved my head and began my fast.

During the time we had walked together the woman and I had come to love one another so much that we did not want to part; but man does not control life, not even his own, and so I had to fulfill my obligation. For many days, I took nothing in my mouth except a few sips of water. As I grew weak, she slipped from my embrace, and her spirit, ever more ethereal, did not weigh upon me as before. After five days, while I dozed, she took her first steps, but she was not ready to continue her journey alone, and she returned to me. She repeated those brief travels on several occasions, each time venturing a little farther. The sorrow of her parting was as terrible as a deep burn, and I had to call on all the courage I had learned from my father not to call her name aloud and bring her back to me forever. After twelve days I dreamed that she was flying like a toucan above the treetops, and I awakened feeling very light, and wanting to weep. She was gone. I picked up my weapons and walked for many hours until I reached a branch of the river. I walked into the water up to my waist, I speared a small fish with a sharp stick and swallowed it whole, scales, tail and all. I immediately vomited it up with a little blood, it was as it should be. I was not sad now. I had learned that sometimes death is more powerful than love. Then I went to hunt, so I would not return to my village with empty hands.

THE PEACE of WILD THINGS

WENDELL BERRY

When despair for the world grows in me
and I wake in the night at the least sound
in fear of what my life and my children's lives may be,
I go and lie down where the wood drake
rests in his beauty on the water, and the great heron feeds.
I come into the peace of wild things
who do not tax their lives with forethought
of grief. I come into the presence of still water.
And I feel above me the day-blind stars
waiting with their light. For a time
I rest in the grace of the world, and am free.

Unintended Consequences

MOSS-GATHERING

THEODORE ROETHKE

To loosen with all ten fingers held wide and limber
And lift up a patch, dark-green, the kind for lining
  cemetery baskets,
Thick and cushiony, like an old-fashioned doormat,
The crumbling small hollow sticks on the underside mixed
  with roots,
And wintergreen berries and leaves still stuck to the top,
That was moss-gathering.
But something always went out of me when I dug loose
  those carpets
Of green, or plunged to my elbows in the spongy yellow-
  ish moss of the marshes:
And afterwards I always felt mean, jogging back over the
  logging road,
As if I had broken the natural order of things in that
  swampland;
Disturbed some rhythm, old and of vast importance,
By pulling off flesh from the living planet;
As if I had committed, against the whole scheme of life, a
  desecration.

The [House] of Life

ROBERT M. HAZEN &
JAMES TREFIL

Most biologists study life by tackling a small, manageable system —
one organ, one cell, or even one molecule. But living systems never
occur in isolation. Life requires the complex interaction of many
organisms with their surrounding environment. Organisms cooper-
ate and compete, eat or are eaten. Life on earth, along with its nonliving environment, functions as a unit, obeying all the physical and
biological principles. You have to study the whole, integrated system
if you want to understand our planet, and this is where the science of
ecology (a word derived from the Greek term for "house") enters the
picture. Ecologists study ecosystems, so they concern themselves
with all the organisms in a given area and their physical environment.

An ecosystem encompasses no fixed size. Almost any chunk
of our planet that includes minerals, air, water, plants, animals, and
microorganisms that interact will qualify. An ecosystem could be a
swamp, a square yard of meadow, a sand dune, a coral reef, or an
aquarium. Natural ecosystems seldom have sharp boundaries: forests
merge into fields, shallow water grades into deep water.

Within an ecosystem, each organism fits like a gear in a complex machine. Each organism depends on its fellows, but performs
necessary functions for them as well. Termites in a forest depend on
trees to produce deadwood, for example, and the trees depend on the
termites to clear the ground for new seedlings. The special place
occupied by an organism in an ecosystem is called its ecological
niche.

All living things on our planet exist in a thin layer at the
surface, a layer that extends only a few hundred yards below the solid

surface and a few miles into the air. We call this region the biosphere, and it can be thought of as the earth's largest ecosystem.

There is one rule that seems to emerge from studies of ecosystems, a rule that follows from the complexity of the web that connects living and nonliving things. It can be stated simply:

You can't change just one thing.

More grandiloquently, it is:

The Law of Unintended Consequences.

No matter how it's stated, the rule comes down to this: in a complex system it is not always possible to predict what the consequences of any change will be, at least with the present state of knowledge. This means that seemingly small changes in ecosystems can cause large effects, while huge changes might leave the system pretty much as it was.

Having made this point, we should also note that life on earth has survived many wild swings in environment in the past. Nature itself is constantly changing the global environment, so that change in and of itself is not necessarily an evil thing, and it's certainly not "unnatural." Nevertheless, the fact remains that we cannot presently predict with certainty what the ultimate effect of any given change will be.

Fable for
TOMORROW

RACHEL CARSON

There was once a town in the heart of America where all life seemed to live in harmony with its surroundings. The town lay in the midst of a checkerboard of prosperous farms, with fields of grain and hillsides of orchards where, in spring, white clouds of bloom drifted above the green fields. In autumn, oak and maple and birch set up a blaze of colour that flamed and flickered across a backdrop of pines. Then foxes barked in the hills and deer silently crossed the fields, half hidden in the mists of the fall mornings.

Along the roads, laurel, viburnum and alder, great ferns and wildflowers delighted the traveller's eye through much of the year. Even in winter the roadsides were places of beauty where countless birds came to feed on the berries and on the seed heads of the dried weeds rising above the snow. The countryside was, in fact, famous for the abundance and variety of its bird life, and when the flood of migrants was pouring through in spring and fall people travelled from great distances to observe them. Others came to fish the streams, which flowed clear and cold out of the hills and contained shady pools where trout lay. So it had been from the days many years ago when the first settlers raised their houses, sank their wells, and built their barns.

Then a strange blight crept over the area and everything began to change. Some evil spell had settled on the community: mysterious maladies swept the flocks of chickens; the cattle and sheep sickened and died. Everywhere was a shadow of death. The farmers spoke of much illness among their families. In the town the doctors had become more and more puzzled by new kinds of sickness appearing among their patients. There had been several sudden and unexplained deaths, not only among adults but even among children, who would be stricken suddenly while at play and die within a few hours.

There was a strange stillness. The birds, for example — where had they gone? Many people spoke of them, puzzled and disturbed. The feeding stations in the backyards were deserted. The few birds seen anywhere were moribund; they trembled violently and could not fly. It was a spring without voices. On the mornings that had once throbbed with the dawn chorus of robins, catbirds, doves, jays, wrens, and scores of other bird voices there was now no sound; only silence lay over the fields and woods and marsh.

On the farms the hens brooded, but no chicks hatched. The farmers complained that they were unable to raise any pigs — the litters were small and the young survived only a few days. The apple trees were coming into bloom but no bees droned among the blossoms, so there was no pollination and there would be no fruit.

The roadsides, once so attractive, were now lined with browned and withered vegetation as though swept by fire. These, too, were silent, deserted by all living things. Even the streams were now lifeless. Anglers no longer visited them, for all the fish had died.

In the gutters under the eaves and between the shingles of the roofs, a white granular powder still showed a few patches; some weeks before it had fallen like snow upon the roofs and the lawns, the fields and streams.

No witchcraft, no enemy action had silenced the rebirth of new life in this stricken world. The people had done it themselves.

This town does not actually exist, but it might easily have a thousand counterparts in America or elsewhere in the world. I know of no community that has experienced all the misfortunes I describe. Yet every one of these disasters has actually happened somewhere, and many real communities have already suffered a substantial number of them. A grim spectre has crept upon us almost unnoticed, and this imagined tragedy may easily become a stark reality we all shall know.

REPORT

ON THE EARTH-AIR ADDICTS

ROBERT PRIEST

It is said that Earth-Air is at once the sweetest and the most addictive scent there is. That is why Earth has been declared off limits to all our Fair Captains. We have lost too many of them — one scent of it and they abandon everything for the mindless comforts below.

Those who are addicted to Earth-Air often stroll. To stroll is to travel aimlessly — for "pleasure" as they put it. It doesn't matter to the Earth-Air addict — just a change of scenery is enough. For, yes, most of the time the Earth-Air addicts just sit around staring. Just staring and breathing and sighing, examining with intense and seemingly durable curiosity such "fabulous" items as sand, stone, grass, or wave.

To be an Earth-Air addict is to abandon the Star-search. It is to wilfully glut the senses — to bathe incessantly in emanations. Just to go on breathing is enough — just to go on strolling. What a waste of life it is to become just a bag— bellows for this detestable Earth-Air. Yet, whenever our Fair Captains are missing we always find them standing on mountain peaks breathing in the Earth-Air. The wind blows and they're insane. They never want to leave. They want to run down in to the valleys and breathe. They want to breathe all the different scents of the Earth-Air there are. The famed Captain Zenon, for instance, was found, finally, perched over something called a Daffodil, his mind gone, his nostrils flared. Captain Arbox was located in ambergris just rolling and rolling, raving about the "aroma," taking great breasty gusts of it deep into his lungs, and then expelling it with long "musical" sighs that were terrible to hear.

STILL LIFE

Ralph Gustafson

The man from Bell-Canada
Buzz-sawed it,
The white birch leaning
Toward their wires
Irrelevant with good buys,
Urgent appointments
For oral cavities.
I meant the pole
To be moved,
The birch up the hill
Busy with permanent matters.

EDEN

ARTHUR C. CLARKE

"I guess," said Jerry Garfield, cutting the engines, "that this is the end of the line." With a gentle sigh, the underjets faded out; deprived of its air cushion, the scout car *Rambling Wreck* settled down upon the twisted rocks of the Hesperian Plateau.

There was no way forward; neither on its jets nor its tractors could S.5 — to give the *Wreck* its official name — scale the escarpment that lay ahead. The South Pole of Venus was only thirty miles away, but it might have been on another planet. They would have to turn back, and retrace their four-hundred-mile journey through this nightmare landscape.

The weather was fantastically clear, with visibility of almost a thousand yards. There was no need of radar to show the cliffs ahead; for once, the naked eye was good enough. The green auroral light, filtering down through clouds that had rolled unbroken for a million years, gave the scene an underwater appearance, and the way in which all distant objects blurred into the haze added to the impression. Sometimes it was easy to believe that they were driving across a shallow sea bed, and more than once Jerry had imagined that he had seen fish floating overhead.

"Shall I call the ship, and say we're turning back?" he asked.

"Not yet," said Dr. Hutchins. "I want to think."

Jerry shot an appealing glance at the third member of the crew, but found no moral support there. Coleman was just as bad; although the two men argued furiously half the time, they were both scientists and therefore, in the opinion of a hardheaded engineer-navigator, not wholly responsible citizens. If Cole and Hutch had bright ideas about going forward, there was nothing he could do except register a protest.

Hutchins was pacing back and forth in the tiny cabin, studying charts and instruments. Presently he swung the car's searchlight toward the cliffs, and began to examine them carefully with binoculars. Surely, thought Jerry, he doesn't expect me to drive up there! S.5 was a hover-track, not a mountain goat....

Abruptly, Hutchins found something. He released his breath in a sudden explosive gasp, then turned to Coleman.

"Look!" he said, his voice full of excitement. "Just to the left of that black mark! Tell me what you see."

He handed over the glasses, and it was Coleman's turn to stare.

"Well, I'm damned," he said at length. "You were right. There are rivers on Venus. That's a dried-up waterfall."

"So you owe me one dinner at the Bel Gourmet when we get back to Cambridge. With champagne."

"No need to remind me. Anyway, it's cheap at the price. But this still leaves your other theories strictly on the crackpot level."

"Just a minute," interjected Jerry. "What's all this about rivers and waterfalls? Everyone knows they can't exist on Venus. It never gets cold enough on this steam bath of a planet for the clouds to condense."

"Have you looked at the thermometer lately?" asked Hutchins with deceptive mildness.

"I've been slightly too busy driving."

"Then I've news for you. It's down to two hundred and thirty, and still falling. Don't forget — we're almost at the Pole, it's wintertime, and we're sixty thousand feet above the lowlands. All this adds up to a distinct nip in the air. If the temperature drops a few more degrees, we'll have rain. The water will be boiling, of course — but it will be water. And though George won't admit it yet, this puts Venus in a completely different light."

"Why?" asked Jerry, though he had already guessed.

"Where there's water, there may be life. We've been in too much of a hurry to assume that Venus is sterile, merely because the average temperature's over five hundred degrees. It's a lot colder here, and that's why I've been so anxious to get to the Pole. There are lakes up here in the highland, and I want to look at them."

"But boiling water!" protested Coleman. "Nothing could live in that!"

"There are algae that manage it on Earth. And if we've learned one thing since we started exploring the planets, it's this: wherever life has the slightest chance of surviving, you'll find it. This is the only chance it's ever had on Venus."

"I wish we could test your theory. But you can see for yourself — we can't go up that cliff."

"Perhaps not in the car. But it won't be too difficult to climb those rocks even wearing thermosuits. All we need do is walk a few miles toward the Pole; according to the radar maps, it's fairly level once you're over the rim. We could manage in — oh, twelve hours at the most. Each of us has been out for longer than that, in much worse conditions."

That was perfectly true. Protective clothing that had been designed to keep men alive in the Venusian lowlands would have an easy job here, where it was only a hundred degrees hotter than Death Valley in midsummer.

"Well," said Coleman, "you know the regulations. You can't go by yourself, and someone has to stay here to keep contact with the ship. How do we settle it this time — chess or cards?"

"Chess takes too long," said Hutchins, "especially when you two play it." He reached into the chart table and produced a well-worn pack. "Cut them, Jerry."

"Ten of spades. Hope you can beat it, George."

"So do I. Damn — only five of clubs. Well, give my regards to the Venusians."

Despite Hutchins' assurance, it was hard work climbing the escarpment. The slope was not too steep, but the weight of oxygen gear, refrigerated thermosuit, and scientific equipment came to more than a hundred pounds per man. The lower gravity — thirteen percent weaker than Earth's — gave a little help, but not much, as they toiled up screes, rested on ledges to regain breath, and then clambered on again through the submarine twilight. The emerald glow that washed around them was brighter than that of the full moon on

Earth. A moon would have been wasted on Venus, Jerry told himself; it could never have been seen from the surface, there were no oceans for it to rule — and the incessant aurora was a far more constant source of light.

They had climbed more than two thousand feet before the ground levelled out into a gentle slope, scarred here and there by channels that had clearly been cut by running water. After a little searching, they came across a gulley wide and deep enough to merit the name of river bed, and started to walk along it.

"I've just thought of something," said Jerry after they had travelled a few hundred yards. "Suppose there's a storm up ahead of us? I don't feel like facing a tidal wave of boiling water."

"If there's a storm," replied Hutchins a little impatiently, "we'll hear it. There'll be plenty of time to reach high ground."

He was undoubtedly right, but Jerry felt no happier as they continued to climb the gently shelving watercourse. His uneasiness had been growing ever since they had passed over the brow of the cliff and had lost radio contact with the scout car. In this day and age, to be out of touch with one's fellow men was a unique and unsettling experience. It had never happened to Jerry before in all his life; even aboard the *Morning Star*, when they were a hundred million miles from Earth, he could always send a message to his family and get a reply back within minutes. But now, a few yards of rock had cut him off from the rest of mankind; if anything happened to them here, no one would ever know, unless some later expedition found their bodies. George would wait for the agreed number of hours; then he would head back to the ship — alone. I guess I'm not really the pioneering type, Jerry told himself. I like running complicated machines, and that's how I got involved in space flight. But I never stopped to think where it would lead, and now it's too late to change my mind...

They had travelled perhaps three miles toward the Pole, following the meanders of the river bed, when Hutchins stopped to make observations and collect specimens. "Still getting colder!" he said. "The temperature's down to one hundred and ninety-nine. That's far and away the lowest ever recorded on Venus. I wish we could call George and let him know."

Jerry tried all the wave bands; he even attempted to raise the

BEFORE EDEN

ship — the unpredictable ups and downs of the planet's ionosphere sometimes made such long-distance reception possible — but there was not a whisper of a carrier wave above the roar and crackle of the Venusian thunderstorms.

"This is even better," said Hutchins, and now there was real excitement in his voice. "The oxygen concentration's way up — fifteen parts in a million. It was only five back at the car, and down in the lowlands you can scarcely detect it."

"But fifteen in a *million*!" protested Jerry. "Nothing could breathe that!"

"You've got hold of the wrong end of the stick," Hutchins explained. "Nothing does breathe it. Something *makes* it. Where do you think Earth's oxygen comes from? It's all produced by life — by growing plants. Before there were plants on Earth, our atmosphere was just like this one — a mess of carbon dioxide and ammonia and methane. Then vegetation evolved, and slowly converted the atmosphere into something that animals could breathe."

"I see," said Jerry, "and you think that the same process has just started here?"

"It looks like it. Something not far from here is producing oxygen — and plant life is the simplest explanation."

"And where there are plants," mused Jerry, "I suppose you'll have animals, sooner or later."

"Yes," said Hutchins, packing his gear and starting up the gulley, "though it takes a few hundred million years. We may be too soon — but I hope not."

"That's all very well," Jerry answered. "But suppose we meet something that doesn't like us? We've no weapons."

Hutchins gave a snort of disgust.

"And we don't need them. Have you stopped to think what we look like? Any animal would run a mile at the sight of us."

There was some truth in it. The reflecting metal foil of their thermosuits covered them from head to foot like flexible, glittering armour. No insects had more elaborate antennas than those mounted on their helmets and back packs, and the wide lenses through which they stared out at the world looked like blank yet monstrous eyes. Yes, there were few animals on Earth that would stop to argue with such apparitions; but any Venusians might have different ideas.

Jerry was still mulling over this when they came upon the lake. Even at that first glimpse, it made him think not of the life they were seeking, but of death. Like a black mirror, it lay amid a fold of the hills; its far edge was hidden in the eternal mist, and ghostly columns of vapour swirled and danced upon its surface. All it needed, Jerry told himself, was Charon's ferry waiting to take them to the other side — or the Swan of Tuonela swimming majestically back and forth as it guarded the entrance to the Underworld....

Yet for all this, it was a miracle — the first free water that men had ever found on Venus. Hutchins was already on his knees almost in an attitude of prayer. But he was only collecting drops of the precious liquid to examine through his pocket microscope.

"Anything there?" asked Jerry anxiously.

Hutchins shook his head.

"If there is, it's too small to see with this instrument. I'll tell you more when we're back at the ship." He sealed a test tube and placed it in his collecting bag, as tenderly as any prospector who had just found a nugget laced with gold. It might be — it probably was — nothing more than plain water. But it might also be a universe of unknown, living creatures on the first stage of their billion year journey to intelligence.

Hutchins had walked no more than a dozen yards along the edge of the lake when he stopped again, so suddenly that Garfield nearly collided with him.

"What's the matter?" Jerry asked. "Seen something?"

"That dark patch of rock over there. I noticed it before we stopped at the lake."

"What about it? It looks ordinary enough to me."

"*I think it's grown bigger.*"

All his life, Jerry was to remember this moment. Somehow he never doubted Hutchins' statement; by this time he could believe anything, even that rocks could grow. The sense of isolation and mystery, the presence of that dark and brooding lake, the never-ceasing rumble of distant storms and the green flickering of the aurora — all these had done something to his mind, had prepared it to face the incredible. Yet he felt no fear; that would come later.

He looked at the rock. It was about five hundred feet away, as far as he could estimate. In this dim, emerald light it was hard to judge distances or dimensions. The rock — or whatever it was — seemed to be a horizontal slab of almost black material, lying near the crest of a low ridge. There was a second, much smaller, patch of similar material near it; Jerry tried to measure and memorize the gap between them, so that he would have some yardstick to detect any change.

Even when he saw that the gap was slowly shrinking, he still felt no alarm — only a puzzled excitement. Not until it had vanished completely, and he realized how his eyes had tricked him, did that awful feeling of helpless terror strike into his heart.

Here was no growing or moving rocks. What they were watching was a dark tide, a crawling carpet, sweeping slowly but inexorably toward them over the top of the ridge.

The moment of sheer, unreasoning panic lasted, mercifully, no more than a few seconds. Garfield's first terror began to fade as soon as he recognized its cause. For that advancing tide had reminded him, all too vividly, of a story he had read many years ago about the army ants of the Amazon, and the way in which they destroyed everything in their path....

But whatever this tide might be, it was moving too slowly to be a real danger, unless it cut off their line of retreat. Hutchins was staring at it intently through their only pair of binoculars; he was the biologist, and he was holding his ground. No point in making a fool of myself, thought Jerry, by running like a scalded cat, if it isn't necessary.

"For heaven's sake," he said at last, when the moving carpet was only a few hundred yards away and Hutchins had not uttered a word or stirred a muscle. "What *is* it?"

Hutchins slowly unfroze, like a statue coming to life.

"Sorry," he said. "I'd forgotten all about you. It's a plant, of course. At least, I suppose we'd better call it that."

"But it's *moving*!"

"Why should that surprise you? So do terrestrial plants. Ever seen speeded-up movies of ivy in action?"

"That still stays in one place — it doesn't crawl all over the landscape."

"Then what about the plankton plants of the sea? *They* can swim when they have to."

Jerry gave up; in any case, the approaching wonder had robbed him of words.

He still thought of the thing as a carpet — a deep-pile one, ravelled into tassels at the edges. It varied in thickness as it moved; in some parts it was a mere film; in others, it heaped up to a depth of a foot or more. As it came closer and he could see its texture, Jerry was reminded of black velvet. He wondered what it felt like to the touch, then remembered that it would burn his fingers even if it did nothing else to them. He found himself thinking, in the lightheaded nervous reaction that often follows a sudden shock: "If there are any Venusians, we'll never be able to shake hands with them. They'd burn us, and we'd give them frostbite."

So far, the thing had shown no signs that it was aware of their presence. It had merely flowed forward like the mindless tide that it almost certainly was. Apart from the fact that it climbed over small obstacles, it might have been an advancing flood of water.

And then, when it was only ten feet away, the velvet tide checked itself. On the right and the left, it still flowed forward; but dead ahead it slowed to a halt.

"We're being encircled," said Jerry anxiously. "Better fall back, until we're sure it's harmless."

To his relief, Hutchins stepped back at once. After a brief hesitation, the creature resumed its slow advance and the dent in its front line straightened out.

Then Hutchins stepped forward again — and the thing slowly withdrew. Half a dozen times the biologist advanced, only to retreat again, and each time the living tide ebbed and flowed in synchronism with his movements. I never imagined, Jerry told himself, that I'd live to see a man waltzing with a plant....

"Thermophobia," said Hutchins. "Purely automatic reaction. It doesn't like our heat."

"*Our* heat!" protested Jerry. "Why, we're living icicles by comparison."

"Of course — but our suits aren't, and that's all it knows about."

Stupid of me, thought Jerry. When you were snug and cool inside your thermosuit, it was easy to forget that the refrigeration unit on your back was pumping a blast of heat out into the surrounding air. No wonder the Venusian plant had shied away....

"Let's see how it reacts to light," said Hutchins. He switched on his chest lamp, and the green auroral glow was instantly banished by the flood of pure white radiance. Until Man had come to this planet, no white light had ever shone upon the surface of Venus, even by day. As in the seas of Earth, there was only a green twilight, deepening slowly to utter darkness.

The transformation was so stunning that neither man could check a cry of astonishment. Gone in a flash was the deep, sombre black of the thick-piled velvet carpet at their feet. Instead, as far as their lights carried, lay a blazing pattern of glorious, vivid reds, laced with streaks of gold. No Persian prince could ever have commanded so opulent a tapestry from his weavers, yet this was the accidental product of biological forces. Indeed, until they had switched on their floods, these superb colours had not even existed, and they would vanish once more when the alien light of Earth ceased to conjure them into being.

"Tikov was right," murmured Hutchins. "I wish he could have known."

"Right about what?" asked Jerry, though it seemed almost a sacrilege to speak in the presence of such loveliness.

"Back in Russia, fifty years ago, he found that plants living in very cold climates tended to be blue and violet, while those from hot ones were red or orange. He predicted that the Martian vegetation would be violet, and said that if there were plants on Venus they'd be red. Well, he was right on both counts. But we can't stand here all day — we've work to do."

"You're sure it's quite safe?" asked Jerry, some of his caution reasserting itself.

"Absolutely — it can't touch our suits even if it wants to. Anyway, it's moving past us."

That was true. They could see now that the entire creature — if it was a single plant, and not a colony — covered a roughly circular area about a hundred yards across. It was sweeping over the ground, as the shadow of a cloud moves before the wind — and where it had rested, the rocks were pitted with innumerable tiny holes that might have been etched by acid.

"Yes," said Hutchins, when Jerry remarked about this. "That's how some lichens feed; they secrete acids that dissolve rock. But no questions, please — not till we get back to the ship. I've several lifetimes' work here, and a couple of hours to do it in."

This was botany on the run....The sensitive edge of the huge plant-thing could move with surprising speed when it tried to evade them. It was as if they were dealing with an animated flapjack, an acre in extent. There was no reaction — apart from the automatic avoidance of their exhaust heat — when Hutchins snipped samples or took probes. The creature flowed steadily onward over hills and valleys, guided by some strange vegetable instinct. Perhaps it was following some vein of mineral; the geologists could decide that, when they analysed the rock samples that Hutchins had collected both before and after the passage of the living tapestry.

There was scarcely time to think or even to frame the countless questions that their discovery had raised. Presumably these creatures must be fairly common, for them to have found one so quickly. How did they reproduce? By shoots, spores, fission, or some other means? Where did they get their energy? What relatives, rivals, or parasites did they have? This could not be the only form of life on Venus — the very idea was absurd, for if you had one species, you must have thousands....

Sheer hunger and fatigue forced them to a halt at last. The creature they were studying could eat its way around Venus — though Hutchins believed that it never went very far from the lake, as from time to time it approached the water and inserted a long, tubelike tendril into it — but the animals from Earth had to rest.

It was a great relief to inflate the pressurized tent, climb in through the air lock, and strip off their themosuits. For the first time, as they relaxed inside their tiny plastic hemisphere, the true wonder and importance of the discovery forced itself upon their minds. This world around them was no longer the same; Venus was no longer dead — it had joined Earth and Mars.

For life called to life, across the gulfs of space. Everything that grew or moved upon the face of any planet was a portent, a promise that man was not alone in this universe of blazing suns and swirling nebulae. If as yet he had found no companions with whom he could speak, that was only to be expected, for the light-years and the ages still stretched before him, waiting to be explored. Meanwhile, he must guard and cherish the life he found, whether it be upon Earth or Mars or Venus.

So Graham Hutchins, the happiest biologist in the solar system, told himself as he helped Garfield collect their refuse and seal it into a plastic disposal bag. When they deflated the tent and started on the homeward journey, there was no sign of the creature they had been examining. That was just as well; they might have been tempted to linger for more experiments, and already it was getting uncomfortably close to their deadline.

No matter; in a few months they would be back with a team of assistants, far more adequately equipped and with the eyes of the world upon them. Evolution had laboured for a billion years to make this meeting possible; it could wait a little longer.

For a while nothing moved in the greenly glimmering, fog-bound landscape; it was deserted by man and crimson carpet alike. Then, flowing over the wind-carved hills, the creature reappeared. Or perhaps it was another of the same strange species; no one would ever know.

It flowed past the little cairn of stones where Hutchins and Garfield had buried their wastes. And then it stopped.

It was not puzzled, for it had no mind. But the chemical urges that drove it relentlessly over the polar plateau were crying: Here, here! Somewhere close at hand was the most precious of all the foods it needed — phosphorous, the element without which the spark of life could never ignite. It began to nuzzle the rocks, to ooze into the cracks and crannies, to scratch and scrabble with probing tendrils. Nothing that it did was beyond the capacity of any plant or tree on Earth — but it moved a thousand times more quickly, requiring only minutes to reach its goal and pierce through the plastic film.

And then it feasted, on food more concentrated than any it had ever known. It absorbed the carbohydrates and the proteins and the phosphates, the nicotine from the cigarette ends, the cellulose from the paper cups and spoons. All these it broke down and assimilated into its strange body, without difficulty and without harm.

Likewise it absorbed a whole microcosmos of living creatures — the bacteria and viruses which, upon an older planet, had evolved into a thousand deadly strains. Though only a very few could survive in this heat and this atmosphere they were sufficient. As the carpet crawled back to the lake, it carried contagion to all its world. Even as the Morning Star *set course for her distant home, Venus was dying. The films and photographs and specimens that Hutchins was carrying in triumph were more precious even than he knew. They were the only record that would ever exist of life's third attempt to gain a foothold in the solar system.*

Beneath the clouds of Venus, the story of Creation was ended.

BEFORE EDEN

The Scars of Umlungu

SINDIWE MAGONA

My people have their own ways of doing things. We have always had our ways of doing things. "The ones scrubbed in hot water" could not see this when they came. They came — "the ones with coloured eyes" — and found my people living worthwhile lives that were satisfying to them. But the newcomers saw only indolence, ignorance and superstition. They saw nothing commendable, nothing worth preserving, least of all emulating. For them our being alive held no lessons whatsoever. It proved nothing. They had their ways. And, in their eyes, these were far, far superior to ours. So began the destruction of my culture. So began our dying.

My people are a wise people. I do not claim God accorded them special preference in the allocation of grey matter. That would be absurd; as absurd as the claims of superiority made by "the ones without colour," the ones we came to call *umlungu.*

But my people are patient. We have a saying: "These mountains were here when we were born. They will be here long after we are gone." Patiently my people observed the world of which they knew they were a part — equal with the land, the rivers, the trees, the mountains and every other living thing.

Thus my people knew how to flow with nature's rhythm, dance to its tune and harness its forces for their good. They knew about using and using up. They knew that rest is the beginning of restoration, that it brings healing.

How can one stand under the heavens one night, look up at the sky, point out one star and say: "That star is mine!"? My people would have thought anyone mad who suddenly pronounced themselves sole owner of such and such a mountain, valley, river or any other piece of the earth.

They had not learnt the greed that brings fences with it. When, later, the newcomers cut up the land, cut it up until it bled, the stakes driven hard into its very heart, the barbed wire strangling it out of breath, my people found themselves lessened, reduced. They were fenced in. They could no longer heal the land.

The strangers had come with new laws to the land they had "discovered." They imposed these laws on the people they found there and made sure they themselves were not bound by them. They were exclusively for my people. Makhulu used to say to me: "Grandchild of mine, a person has a definite nature, and if something is good you can be sure they will keep it for themselves."

My people could no longer heal the land. They could not restore it when it was exhausted. The law forbade them to move pasture. A person's place of dwelling became their place of dying. We lost freedom of movement — the land lost the right to rest and restoration.

Fenced in. Forced to till exhausted land, we could not feed ourselves. But, you see, even that was no accident. The no-colour people had planned it all. They did nothing without planning it through and through — years in advance.

To feed his children, to feed his wife and his aged parents, a man was forced to go to the ones with eyes that have colour. And beg them to use his strength as they would use a horse. For that they would give him the shiny buttons without holes they had brought with them. This had become the only thing of value. It was hard to come by it. The scrubbed ones made sure they kept it under lock and key all the time. And never gave my people enough to get the things it was supposed to give them: food, clothing, medicine, anything. You could be dying, but without this button *umlungu*, the ones without colour, wouldn't give you medicine.

Umlungu's law said we could not dig for roots: it said we could not gather healing herbs. "Miserly is the white man, indeed. He withholds ochre which he, himself, does not use. *Uyabandeza umlungu. Ude abandeze imbola engayiquabi,*" exclaimed my people, flabbergasted. For this kind of stinginess was new to them.

Ochre is the red powder with which we adorned ourselves. Now it was illegal to dig the ground for it. Resistance was strong, there were infringements galore. But by the time my own mother

SINDIWE MAGONA was a young woman ochre had already become a thing of the past.

Umlungu had an even better way of weaning us from our ways. Backward. Heathen. Things of the dark. Those are some of the labels he gave all things essentially us. The things that defined our uniqueness. In time we learnt to hate them ourselves. To scorn those who adhered to them, who refused to "go with the times," those we saw as hesitant "to enter the world of electricity, the world of light."

Instead of ochre and herbs, roots and other powders we started using *umlungu's* creams. They promised us "eternal youthfulness, glowing, wrinkle-free skin." We didn't stop to think that our skin was already free of wrinkle, well into grand old age. We were being civilized. And happily did we stretch our necks for the yoke.

Umlungu's ways have an essential ingredient called Progress. Where Mama started with Metamorphosa, graduated to Karroo Freckle and Complexion Cream and Bu-tone Cream for a Lovelier Complexion, now, in her nineties, she is on Oil of Ulay, that bona fide fountain of youth.

But Mama is far, far luckier than I am.

I am a true product of *umlungu's* enlightenment. My face never was touched by such crudity as ochre or any of those things rural women — whom, basking in our new-found sophistication, we called backward — used on their faces. I started on Pond's Face Cream as a preteen. I was into Karroo Freckle and Complexion Cream by my adolescence. And in my early twenties, like millions of African women my age, I was breaking new ground. By this time, Progress had brought black people an elixir. Skin Lightening Creams.

And *umlungu* said he was doing what he was doing for our own good. He couldn't understand our gross stupidity. He had a duty to stop us from doing harm to ourselves. The yawning *dongas*[1] crisscrossing the land told *umlungu* it was the women digging for their cosmetics that were to blame; it was our large herds of cattle, the women gathering firewood. So said the *dongas* to *umlungu*.

But, to my people, the bleeding soil sang a different song; a song of mourning. And, in the manner of our tradition, my people passed the history on:

"These white people and their white fences! They have killed the land."

"They came with no cattle. But today we are the ones without cattle, while they boast ever-swelling herds."

"Our land has been stolen. We live in fenced-in toy plots. Look at their farms! We can ride across them for a whole day without reaching the other side."

With hearts more sorrow-filled with each dying day, my people watched their cattle getting thinner, their herds dwindle — and the youth of the nation die in rock falls in the mines of the colourless ones, who made them dig for gold they would never own.

"The land died with the coming of the *umlungu*," said my people. And the mothers wailed: "We lose our sons in mines of greed, mines our eyes have never seen, for gold we never touch."

Young women, their husbands away too long, swallowed by the mines, fretted: "Do not forget me, my love, in the land of gold. Do not forget me, beloved. My heart, daily, yearns for you." We became part-time parents to our children.

The fences built for the colourless ones were not yet finished. There was more to come. *Umlungu* didn't care about the problems he made for my people. What did it matter that a mother, for lack of firewood, could not cook for her children? *Umlungu* had a bigger problem: deforestation.

We had no experience of hoarding, of planning scarcity when there was enough. We had not learnt that one person might exact a price from another. We gave free what God had already given.

Umlungu said he was not starving us. We could always buy firewood. Go to the shop and use the button without holes, he said. His brother who owned the shop wanted plenty of that button. But the button didn't like my people at all. It took one look, made a sharp U-turn and went right back whence it came. The coloured-eyed people hoarded it all. And the gold. And the land. To own. While we still wondered: how can a person claim a star as a personal possession?

Our fathers and our brothers, they toiled hard for that button without a hole. They suffered insults, broke their bodies and lost their lives. The button remained unmoved by our sacrifice. It was of one mind with those who had brought it. It would never change allegiance.

SINDIWE MAGONA   Poor as we were — my generation of women — we used a lot of buttons without holes buying the creams that bleached our skin. We listened to *umlungu's* promises of a better life. If only we could rid ourselves or our colour, scour it off, like some dirty foreign matter. How we pursued the dream! At last we would be like them, the people who had brought us all these things of light. How we "chased" the mirage: Ambi Skin Lightening Cream, Super Rose, Clear Tone, Astra... and others too many to list here.

Like the fences on the land the creams made *umlungu* plenty, plenty of buttons without holes... and killed our skin. Just like the fences that killed the land. Today thousands of us walk around with ugly dark blotches on our faces, a disfigurement. The land has the scarring *dongas* and we have these hideous marks.

We have no name for this disease in my language, or in any of the indigenous languages of the land. "Chloasma" *umlungu* calls that which sits on our faces like fungus on a plant. Chloasma. And he has a cure for it. If you can give him many many... buttons without a hole.

1 steep-sided gullies created by soil erosion.

THE Wound

HOWARD FAST

Max Gaffey always insisted that the essence of the oil industry could be summed up in a simple statement: the right thing in the wrong place. My wife, Martha, always disliked him and said that he was a spoiler. I suppose he was, but how was he different from any of us in that sense? We were all spoilers, and if we were not the actual thing, we invested in it and thereby became rich. I myself had invested the small nest egg that a college professor puts away in a stock Max Gaffey gave me. It was called Thunder Inc., and the company's function was to use atomic bombs to release natural gas and oil locked up in the vast untouched shale deposits that we have here in the United States.

Oil shale is not a very economical source of oil. The oil is locked up in the shale, and about sixty percent of the total cost of shale oil consists of the laborious methods of mining the shale, crushing it to release the oil, and then disposing of the spent shale.

Gaffey sold to Thunder Inc. an entirely new method, which involved the use of surplus atomic bombs for the release of shale oil. In very simplistic terms, a deep hole is bored in shale-oil deposits. Then an atomic bomb is lowered to the bottom of the hole, after which the hole is plugged and the bomb is detonated. Theoretically, the heat and force of the atomic explosion crushes the shale and releases the oil to fill the underground cavern formed by the gigantic force of the bomb. The oil does not burn because the hole is sealed, and thereby, for a comparatively small cost, untold amounts of oil can be tapped and released — enough perhaps to last until that time when we experience a complete conversion to atomic energy — so vast are the shale deposits.

Such at least was the way Max Gaffey put the proposition to me, in a sort of mutual brainpicking operation. He had the utmost admiration for my knowledge of the Earth's crust, and I had an equally profound admiration for his ability to make two or five or ten dollars appear where only one had been before.

HOWARD FAST   My wife disliked him and his notions, and most of all the proposal to feed atomic bombs into the Earth's crust.

"It's wrong," she said flatly. "I don't know why or how, but this I do know, that everything connected with that wretched bomb is wrong."

"Yet couldn't you look at this as a sort of salvation?" I argued. "Here we are in the United States with enough atom bombs to destroy life on ten earths the size of ours — and every one of these bombs represents an investment of millions of dollars. I could not agree more when you hold that those bombs are the most hideous and frightful things the mind of man ever conceived.

"Then how on Earth can you speak of salvation?"

"Because so long as those bombs sit here, they represent a constant threat — day and night the threat that some feather-brained general or brainless politician will begin the process of throwing them at out neighbours. But here Gaffey has come up with a peaceful use for the bomb. Don't you see what that means?"

"I'm afraid I don't," Martha said.

"It means that we can use the damn bombs for something other than suicide — because if this starts, it's the end of mankind. But there are oil-shale and gas-shale deposits all over the Earth, and if we can use the bomb to supply man with a century of fuel, not to mention the chemical byproducts, we may just find a way to dispose of those filthy bombs."

"Oh, you don't believe that for a moment,"Martha snorted.

"I do. I certainly do."

And I think I did. I went over the plans that Gaffey and his associates had worked out, and I could not see any flaw. If the hole were plugged properly, there would be no fallout. We knew that and we had the know-how to plug the hole, and we had proven it in at least twenty underground explosions. The Earth tremor would be inconsequential; in spite of the heat, the oil would not ignite, and in spite of the cost of the atom bombs, the savings would be monumental. In fact, Gaffey hinted that some accommodation between the government and Thunder Inc. was in the process of being worked out, and if it went through as planned, the atom bombs might just cost Thunder Inc. nothing at all, the whole thing being in the way of an experiment for the social good.

After all, Thunder Inc. did not own any oil-shale deposits, nor was it in the oil business. It was simply a service organization with the proper know-how, and for a fee — if the process worked — it would release the oil for others. What that fee would be was left unsaid, but Max Gaffey, in return for my consultation, suggested that I might buy a few shares, not only of Thunder Inc., but of General Shale Holdings.

I had altogether about ten thousand dollars in savings available and another ten thousand in American Telephone and government bonds. Martha had a bit of money of her own, but I left that alone, and without telling her, I sold my Telephone stock and my bonds. Thunder Inc. was selling at five dollars a share, and I bought two thousand shares. General Shale was selling for two dollars, and I bought four thousand shares. I saw nothing immoral — as business morality was calculated — in the procedures adopted by Thunder Inc. Its relationship to the government was no different than the relationships of various other companies, and my own process of investment was perfectly straightforward and honourable. I was not even the recipient of secret information, for the first atom-bomb-shale-oil proposal had been widely publicized if little believed.

Even before the first test explosion was undertaken, the stock of Thunder Inc. went from five to sixty-five dollars a share. My ten thousand dollars became one hundred and thirty thousand, and that doubled again a year later. The four thousand shares of General Shale went up to eighteen dollars a share; and from a modestly poor professor I became a moderately rich professor. When finally, almost two years after Max Gaffey first approached me, they exploded the first atom bomb in a shaft reamed in the oil-shale deposits, I had abandoned the simple anxieties of the poor and had developed an entirely new set tailored for the upper-middle class. We became a two-car family, and a reluctant Martha joined me in shopping for a larger house. In the new house, Gaffey and his wife came to dinner, and Martha armed herself with two stiff martinis. Then she was quietly polite until Gaffey began to talk about the social good. He painted a bright picture of what shale oil could do and how rich we might well become.

"Oh yes —yes," Martha agreed. "Pollute the atmosphere,

kill more people with more cars, increase the speed with which we can buzz around in circles and get precisely nowhere."

"Oh, you're a pessimist,"said Gaffey's wife, who was young and pretty but no mental giant.

"Of course there are two sides to it," Gaffey admitted. "It's a question of controls. You can't stop progress, but it seems to me that you can direct it."

"The way we've been directing it —so that our rivers stink and our lakes are sewers of dead fish and our atmosphere is polluted and our birds poisoned by DDT and our natural resources are spoiled. We are all spoilers, aren't we?"

"Come now," I protested, "this is the way it is, and all of us are indignant about it, Martha."

"Are you really?"

"I think so."

"Men have always dug in the earth," Gaffey said. "Otherwise we'd still be in the Stone Age."

"And perhaps a good bit happier."

"No, no, no," I said, "The Stone Age was a very unpleasant time, Martha. You don't wish us back there."

"Do you remember," Martha said slowly, "how there was a time when men used to speak about the Earth our mother? It was Mother Earth, and they believed it. She was the source of life and being."

"She still is."

"You've sucked her dry," Martha said curiously. "When a woman is sucked dry, her children perish."

It was an odd and poetical thing to say, and, as I thought, in bad taste. I punished Martha by leaving Mrs. Gaffey with her, with the excuse that Max and I had some business matters to discuss, which indeed we did. We went into the new study in the new house and we lit fifty-cent cigars, and Max told me about the thing they had aptly named "Project Hades."

"The point is," Max said, "that I can get you into this at the very beginning. At the bottom. There are eleven companies involved — very solid and reputable companies" — he named them, and I was duly impressed — "who are putting up the capital for what will be a subsidiary of Thunder Inc. For their money they get a twenty-five percent interest. There is also ten percent, in the form of stock warrants, put aside for consultation and advice, and you will understand why. I can fit you in for one-and-a-half percent — roughly three quarters of a million — simply for a few weeks of your time, and we will pay all expenses, plus an opinion."

"It sounds interesting."

"It should sound more than that. If Project Hades works, your interest will increase tenfold within a matter of five years. It's the shortest cut to being a millionaire that I know."

"All right — I'm more than interested. Go on."

Gaffey took a map of Arizona out of his pocket, unfolded it, and pointed to a marked-off area. "Here," he said, "is what should —according to all our geological knowledge — be one of the richest oil-bearing areas in the country. Do you agree?"

"Yes, I know the area," I replied. "I've been over it. Its potential is purely theoretical. No one has ever brought in anything there —not even salt water. It's dry and dead."

"Why?"

I shrugged. "That's the way it is. If we could locate oil through geological premise and theory, you and I would both be richer than Getty. The fact of the matter is, as you well know, that sometimes it's there and sometimes it isn't. More often it isn't."

"Why? We know our job. We drill in the right places."

"What are you getting at, Max?"

"A speculation — particularly for this area. We have discussed this speculation for months. We have tested it as best we can. We have examined it from every possible angle. And now we are ready to blow about five million dollars to test our hypotheses — providing —"

"Providing what?"

"That your expert opinion agrees with ours. In other words, we've cast the die with you. You look at the situation and tell us go ahead — we go ahead. You look at it and tell us it's a crock of beans — well, we fold our tents like the Arabs and silently steal away."

"Just on my say-so?"

"Just on your brains and know-how."

"Max, aren't you barking up the wrong tree? I'm a simple professor of geology at an unimportant western state university, and there are at least twenty men in the field who can teach me the right time —"

"Not in our opinion. Not on where the stuff is. We know who's in the field and we know their track records. You keep your light under a bushel, but we know what we want. So don't argue. It's either a deal or it isn't. Well?"

"How the devil can I answer you when I don't even know what you're talking about?"

"All right — I'll spell it out , quick and simple. The oil was there once, right where it should be. Then a natural convulsion — a very deep fault. The Earth cracked and the oil flowed down, deep down, and now giant pockets of it are buried there where no drill can reach them."

"How deep?"

"Who knows? Fifteen, twenty miles."

"That's deep."

"Maybe deeper. When you think of that kind of distance under the surface, you're in a darker mystery than Mars or Venus — all of which you know."

"All of which I know." I had a bad, uneasy feeling, and some of it must have shown in my face.

"What's wrong?'

"I don't know. Why don't you leave it alone, Max?"

"Why?"

"Come on, Max — we're not talking about drilling for oil. Fifteen, twenty miles. There' s a rig down near the Pecos in Texas and they've just passed the twenty-five thousand foot level, and that's about it. Oh, maybe another thousand, but you're talking about oil that's buried in one hundred thousand feet of crust. You can't drill for it; you can only go in and —"

"And what?"

"Blast it out."

"Of course —and how do you fault us for that? What's wrong with it? We know — or at least we have good reason to believe —that there's a fissure that opened and closed. The oil should be under tremendous pressure. We put in an atom bomb —a bigger bomb than we ever used before — and we blast that fissure open again.... That should be the biggest gusher in all the history of gushers."

"You've drilled the hole already, haven't you, Max?"

"That's right."

"How deep?"

"Twenty-two thousand feet."

"And you have a bomb?"

Max nodded. "We have the bomb. We've been working on this for five years, and seven months ago the boys in Washington cleared the bomb. It's out there in Arizona waiting —"

"For what?"

"For you to look everything over and tell us to go ahead."

"Why? We have enough oil —"

"Like hell we have! You know damn well why — and do you imagine we can drop it now after all the money and time that's been invested in this?"

"You said you'd drop it if I said so."

"As a geologist in our pay, and I know you well enough to know what that means in terms of your professional skill and pride."

I stayed up half that night talking with Martha about it and trying to fit it into some kind of moral position. But the only thing I could come up with was the fact that here was one less atom bomb to murder man and destroy the life of the Earth, and that I could not argue with. A day later I was at the drilling site in Arizona.

The spot was well chosen. From every point of view this was an oil explorer's dream, and I suppose that fact had been duly noted for the past half century, for there were the moldering remains of a hundred futile rigs, rotting patterns of wooden and metal sticks as far as one could see, abandoned shacks, trailers left with lost hopes, ancient trucks, rusting gears, piles of abandoned pipe —all testifying to the hope that springs eternal in the wildcatter's breast.

Thunder Inc. was something else, a great installation in the middle of the deep valley, a drilling rig larger and more complex than any I had ever seen, a wall to contain the oil should they fail to cap it immediately, a machine shop, a small generating plant, at least a hundred vehicles of various sorts, and perhaps fifty mobile homes.

THE WOUND

HOWARD FAST   The very extent and vastness of the action here deep in the badlands was breathtaking; and I let Max know what I thought of his statement that all this would be abandoned if I said that the idea was worthless.

"Maybe yes — maybe no. What *do* you say?"

"Give me time."

"Absolutely, all the time you want."

Never have I been treated with such respect. I prowled all over the place and I rode a jeep around and about and back and forth and up into the hills and down again; but no matter how long I prowled and sniffed and estimated, mine would be no more than an educated guess. I was also certain that they would not give up the project if I disapproved and said that it would be a washout. They believed in me as a sort of oil-dowser, especially if I told them to go ahead. What they were really seeking was an expert's affirmation of their own faith. And that was apparent from the fact that they had already drilled an expensive twenty-two-thousand foot hole and had set up all this equipment. If I told them they were wrong, their faith might be shaken a little, but they would recover and find themselves another dowser.

I told this to Martha when I telephoned her.

"Well, what do you honestly think?"

"It's oil country. But I'm not the first one to come up with that brilliant observation. The point is — does their explanation account for the lack of oil?"

"Does it?"

"I don't know. No one knows. And they're dangling a million dollars right in front of my nose."

"I can't help you," Martha said. "You've got to play this one yourself."

Of course she couldn't help me. No one could have helped me. It was too far down, too deeply hidden. We knew what the other side of the Moon looked like and we knew something about Mars and other planets, but what have we ever known about ourselves and the place where we live?

The day after I spoke to Martha, I met with Max and his board of directors. "I agree," I told them. "The oil should be there. My opinion is that you should go ahead and try the blast."

They questioned me after that for about an hour, but when you play the role of a dowser, questions and answers become a sort of magical ritual. The plain fact of the matter is that no one had ever exploded a bomb of such power at such a depth, and until it was done, no one knew what would happen.

I watched the preparations for the explosion with great interest. The bomb, with its implosion casing, was specially made for this task — or remade would be a better way of putting it — very long, almost twenty feet, very slim. It was armed after it was in the rigging, and then the board of directors, engineers, technicians, newspapermen, Max, and myself retreated to the concrete shelter and control station, which had been built almost a mile away from the shaft. Closed-circuit television linked us with the hole; and while no one expected the explosion to do any more than jar the Earth heavily at the surface, the Atomic Energy Comission specified the precautions we took.

We remained in the shelter for five hours while the bomb made its long descent — until at last our instruments told us that it rested on the bottom of the drill hole. Then we had a simple countdown, and the chairman of the board pressed the red button. Red and white buttons are man's glory. Press a white button and a bell rings or an electric light goes on; press a red button and the hellish force of a sun comes into being — this time five miles beneath the Earth's surface.

Perhaps it was this part and point in the Earth's surface; perhaps there was no other place where exactly the same thing would have happened; perhaps the fault that drained away the oil was a deeper fault than we had ever imagined. Actually we will never know; we only saw what we saw, watching through the closed-circuit TV. We saw the Earth swell. The swell rose up like a bubble — a bubble about two hundred yards in diameter — and then the surface of the bubble dissipated in a column of dust or smoke that rose up perhaps five hundred feet from the valley bottom, stayed a moment with the lowering sun behind it, like the very column of fire out of Sinai, and then lifted whole and broke suddenly in the wind. Even in the shelter we heard the screaming rumble of sound, and as the face of the enormous hole that the dust had left cleared, there bubbled up a column of oil perhaps a hundred feet in diameter. Or was it oil?

HOWARD FAST   The moment we saw it, a tremendous cheer went up in the shelter, and the cheer cut off in its own echo. Our closed-circuit system was colour television, and this column of oil was bright red.

"Red oil," someone whispered. Then it was quiet.

"When can we get out?" someone else demanded.

"Another ten minutes."

The dust was up and away in the opposite direction, and for ten minutes we stood and watched the bright red oil bubble out of the hole, forming a great pond within the retaining walls, and filling the space with amazing rapidity and lapping over the walls, for the flow must have been a hundred thousand gallons a second or even more, and then outside of the walls and a thickness of it all across the valley floor, rising so quickly that from above, where we were, we saw that we would be cut off from the entire installation. At that point we didn't wait, but took our chances with the radiation and raced down the desert hillside toward the hole and the mobile homes and the trucks — but not quickly enough. We came to a stop at the edge of a great lake of red oil. "It's not red oil," someone said.

"Damn it, it's not oil!"

"The hell it's not! It's oil!"

We were moving back as it spread and rose and covered the trucks and houses, and then it reached a gap in the valley and poured through and down across the desert, into the darkness of the shadows that the big rocks threw — flashing red in the sunset and later black in the darkness. Someone touched it and put a hand to his mouth.

"It's blood."

Max was next to me. "He's crazy," Max said.

Someone else said that it was blood.

I put a finger into the red fluid and raised it to my nose. It was warm, almost hot, and there was no mistaking the smell of hot, fresh blood. I tasted it with the tip of my tongue.

"What is it?" Max whispered.

The others gathered around now — silent, with the red sun setting across the red lake and the red reflected on our faces, our eyes glinting with the red. "God, what is it?" Max demanded.

"It's blood," I replied.

"From where?" Then we were all silent.

We spent the night on the top of the butte where the shelter had been built, and in the morning, all around us, as far as we could see, there was a hot, steaming sea of red blood, the smell so thick and heavy that we were all sick from it; and all of us vomited half a dozen times before the helicopters came for us and took us away.

The day after I returned home, Martha and I were sitting in the living room, she with a book and I with the paper, where I had read about their trying to cap the thing, except that even with diving suits they could not get down to where it was; and she looked up from her book and said:

"Do you remember that thing about the mother?"

"What thing?"

"A very old thing. I think I heard once that it was half as old as time, or maybe a Greek fable or something of the sort — but anyway, the mother has one son, who is the joy of her heart and all the rest that a son could be to a mother, and then the son falls in love or under the spell of a beautiful and wicked woman — very wicked and very beautiful. And he desires to please her, oh, he does indeed, and he says to her, "Whatever you desire I will bring it to you —"

"Which is nothing to say to any woman, but ever," I put in.

"I won't quarrel with that," Martha said mildly, "because when he does put it to her, she replies that what she desires most on this Earth is the living heart of his mother, plucked from her breast. So what does this worthless and murderous idiot male do but race home to his mother, and then out with the knife, ripping her breast to belly and tearing the living heart out of her body —"

"I don't like your story."

"— and with the heart in his hand he blithely dashes back toward his ladylove. But on the way through the forest he catches his toe on a root, stumbles, and falls headlong, the mother's heart knocked out of his hand. And as he pulls himself up and approaches the heart, it says to him, "Did you hurt yourself when you fell, my son?"

"Lovely story. What does it prove?"

"Nothing, I suppose. Will they ever stop the bleeding? Will they close the wound?"

"I don't think so."

"Then will your mother bleed to death?"

"My mother?"

"Yes."

"Oh."

"My mother," Martha said. "Will she bleed to death?"

"I suppose so."

"That's all you can say — I suppose so?"

"What else?"

"Suppose you had told them not to go ahead?"

"You asked me that twenty times, Martha. I told you. They would have gotten another dowser."

"And another? And another?"

"Yes."

"Why?" she cried out. "For God's sake, why?"

"I don't know."

"But you lousy men know everything else."

"Mostly we only know how to kill it. That's not everything else. We never learned to make anything alive."

"And now it's too late," Martha said.

"It's too late, yes." I agreed, and I went back to reading the paper. But Martha just sat there, the book open in her lap, looking at me; and then after a while she closed the book and went upstairs to bed.

REQUIEM
FOR A RIVER

Kim Williams

"So we diverted the river," he said,
showing blueprints
and maps
and geological surveys.
"It'll go in this canal now."

The Rio Blanco River starts in a glacier
up the white-capped Andes.
It has run through a green valley
for three million years,
maybe more.

Now in this year
when the Rio Blanco copper mine
at 12,000 feet altitude
gets underway,
the river has to go.

Pick it up,
Move it over —
Anything is possible.
Don't stand in the way
of progress,
And a 90-million-dollar mine.
"We concreted the dam," Bert said.

Thanks.

ᴛᴀʟᴋɪɴɢ GARBAGE

LASANDA KURUKULASURIYA

"Reduce! Re-use! Recycle!" The message hits Canadian consumers through all the media, including — ironically enough — the junk mail. "Don't use all those plastic bags! Don't choke fruit and vegetables with plastic! Buy loose!"

As newcomers from Sri Lanka we try to absorb the barrage and we compare it with the situation back home. We may not be the most environmentally concerned citizens in the world. But compared with this we do not have a garbage problem — yet.

Like many shoppers in Colombo, my partner Shahid and I used to have a cane basket we took along with us to the Sunday fair or *pola* every week. No environmentalist could have complained about it. I liked the basket in a way I could not possibly have liked a plastic bag. My cat liked it too, and I had a tough time keeping him from sleeping in it.

You need a good sturdy basket at the *pola*. There are no supermarket carts to push around. Most items — rice, flour, lentils, vegetables, fruit, biscuits, eggs — are bought loose or wrapped in newspaper. If you want a plastic bag you usually have to pay for it. At most we would carry one plastic bag separately. For eggs we took a reusable plastic tray along with us.

Sri Lankan children still carry reusable, litter-free plastic drink bottles to school. The obnoxious "Tetra-Pak," that square juice pack with a layer of aluminum inside, a layer of plastic outside and cardboard in between, has yet to make its appearance. Coca Cola, Fanta, and Sprite have all but usurped the local competition in the soft drink industry, but reusable glass bottles are still very much the norm. When income levels are low, people need to buy in small quantities — large, two-litre plastic containers don't move fast enough. It is quite normal to ask for a single envelope or cigarette, two eggs or 100 grams of sugar at the ubiquitous "boutiques" that thrive on every street corner.

Neither a vendor nor a householder likes to feel short-changed for want of a little power of persuasion. There was an orange seller who dropped by our home every so often. Even before he walked through the gate he would announce his — astronomical —opening price, complete with an explanation: unique, quality, absolute scarcity, market fluctuations and so on.

Walking into the shade he would place his basket on the ground, taking his time, mopping his brow — to await the usual response. "Are you out of your mind?" would be the next reaction. "No oranges today. No time. We are leaving now." Then came a protracted debate on the size, shape, colour, sweetness, juiciness, and any other special features of the oranges present, with cross references to oranges past, their relative worth in rupees and cents.

During the course of this weighty business either party might at any time take a break to gaze at the sky, swear at the heat or bow the head to ponder on the eternal verities of life. As the final price drew near our vendor would magnanimously drop the price a full 50 cents and *voilá!* a sale would be made.

The point is that, for the most part, middle class urban consumers in Sri Lanka still cannot afford the *luxury* of waste. Most people do not buy more from the grocers than they know they will actually consume. They re-use whatever they can and are loath to discard bags, jars, tins, or boxes that can be put to other uses. Colombo's poshest gardens are still manured with cattle dung, compost, and used tea leaves.

There is no equivalent in Colombo to Toronto's "Blue-box" progam for recycling paper. But most people save newspaper anyway, to be sold to the "paper man" — an institution as old as newspapers themselves. The "paper man" disturbs your Sunday afternoon with his unintelligible cry (it means "Papers, bottles!") as he strolls down the road balancing a neatly folded bag on his head. Tucked in at the waist of his sarong is a metal scale, which he uses to weigh the papers in lots on your doorstep. Empty bottles are valued on a case-by-case basis. The 50 or 100 rupees you might make on the deal is easily enough to take you to the movies. The paper man sells to wholesale traders, who in turn sell to the "boutiques," which use it to wrap the items they sell.

I don't want to give a false impression of a cozy, picture-perfect,

LASANDA KURUKULASURIYA   small-town paradise. Environment is a sorely neglected issue in Sri Lanka. Colombo does have a garbage disposal problem. But it is largely caused, I suspect, by municipal inefficiency rather than the volume of garbage. Excess packaging has not reached anything like the proportions of the crisis in North America.

But in recent years Western-style supermarkets have begun to spring up in Colombo. They hold out the promise of clean, efficient, streamlined — and impersonal — service to customers. A range of imported products, dressed up in their layers of attractive, colourful packaging, beckons from the shelves. These are the very products that demand your attention on the TV advertisements. Along with them Sri Lanka, like so many other developing countries, may have imported a problem that once never existed.

For the time being the big supermarkets are places where only the elite can shop. The over-riding need for thrift and economy prevents middle-class consumers from patronizing them. Soon, though, supermarket shopping may well become the order of the day in the cities. Then it can only be a matter of time before Sri Lanka has to appeal to some Western government for aid so that it can develop techniques for environmentally-friendly product packaging.

THE FABLE

of the Dodo

DAVID DAY

Once upon a time, on an island far away, there was the strangest bird you've ever seen. It was large and round, and had a rather weirdly comic face. It had wings, but was so fat it could not fly. It was so stupid, it did not have the sense to flee its enemies. It is no surprise that soon after its discovery, this ridiculous bird became extinct.

This is a brief potted version of what passes for a typical history of that creature we call the Dodo (*Raphus cucullatus*). However, this is a view of the bird that is neither fair to the animal nor historically accurate.

In the three centuries since its extinction, the Dodo has become as much of a mythical animal as a unicorn or a dragon. Because of its seemingly awkward and comic shape, and the manner in which it so rapidly became extinct after its discovery, it has become the butt of many a joke: "Dead as a Dodo" and "Dumb as a Dodo" are as commonplace as "Sly as a Fox" and "Meek as a Lamb."

It is a pointless exercise to defend this long-lost animal from such jibes, but there is some importance in learning from the errors of history. Unfortunately, as it is usually told, the history of the Dodo is not so much history as an extremely misleading fable about obsolete evolutionary design. The Dodo is generally shown as the classic example of that much misinterpreted phrase "survival of the fittest." This fable of the Dodo implies that the animal was simply "unfit" for survival and, far from being tragic, there was a moral "rightness" in its extinction.

It is a view of history that allows us to forget the circumstances behind the Dodo's case and the human role in its extinction. It argues that it was a law of nature itself that exterminated the Dodo. It is a view that ignores the fact that the Dodo had survived on this planet for sixty million years before it encountered the human race. This is some thirty times longer than humans have been on earth. How could such an "unfit" animal survive for so long?

This convenient interpretation of the idea of "survival of the fittest" as presented in this modern "fable of the Dodo" has been used to justify the hundreds of other man-caused animal extinctions that have occurred over the last three centuries. It is a view that is impossible to uphold with any honesty if we look at the actual historic facts. In almost every case, but for the actions of the human race, there is no doubt that all these species would still survive today.

Still, a very good place to begin to review the natural history of extinction over the last three centuries is with that most infamous of cases: the Dodo.

Six hundred miles off the east coast of Madagascar lies an isolated trio of beautiful islands known as the Mascarenes — Mauritius, Réunion, and Rodriguez. Set alone in the Indian Ocean, the islands were rarely visited by man until early in the sixteenth century. In common with many other remote islands, no mammals lived on the Mascarenes, leaving the birds there free to live without fear of predators. In time, the birds came to dominate the islands, taking advantage of their remarkably safe, isolated habitat to evolve into many strange, wonderful species. One of these species was the Dodo.

Strange as it may seem, the Dodo was actually a giant form of flightless dove. At 23kg (50lb) in weight it was about the size of two turkeys, and certainly the largest "pigeon" to inhabit the earth. The Dodo had a large head which was only partially feathered. It had a strong, hooked beak and its large body was rounded and feathered with a soft, dark down. It had strong, stout legs and small, flightless wings. The Dodo was extremely dove-like and gentle in its temperament and yet for tens of millions of years it not only survived, but became one of the dominant life forms in this island paradise of Mauritius.

When the Portugese arrived on Mauritius in 1507, the Dodos had never seen man, or any form of predatory mammal, before. Living as they did, on a lonely island inhabited mostly by birds, they had no fear whatever. When the sailors came ashore from these first tall ships, the Dodos came wandering out of the undergrowth and on to the beach to inspect these curious-looking creatures. The reaction of the sailors was immediate: they slaughtered the trusting, inquisitive birds on sight.

The Dodo's innocent, curious nature was neither unique nor due to stupidity: in sixty million years they had never experienced anything more aggressive than the plant-eating giant tortoises that crawled up on the island's beaches. Similar reactions of numerous species were frequently recorded by travellers to uninhabited tropical islands. Furthermore, it is a curious fact that, in every case, when European travellers came upon a tropical island that had never been visited by humans before, they constantly delighted in exclaiming that they had found an idyllic paradise. They would then immediately set about slaughtering its every inhabitant.

Typical was this remarkable account written in 1788 by Surgeon Arthur Bowes aboard the British ship *Lady Penrhyn* that visited a newly discovered tropical island: "When I was in the woods among the birds I could not help picturing myself in the Golden Age described by Ovid — all these birds walking totally fearless and unconcerned in all parts around us so that we had nothing more to do than stand still a minute or two and knock down as many as we pleased, if you missed they would never run away. The pigeons were so tame they would sit upon the branches of the trees till you might go and take them off with your hands. Many hundreds of parrots and paroquets, magpies and other birds were caught and carried aboard our ship."

Another sailor, Captain Thomas *Charlotte*, in another British ship called the Charlotte but on the same expedition as Surgeon Bowes, also wrote about the birds on that island on the same day: "Several of these I knocked down, and their legs being broken, I placed them near me as I sat under a tree. The pain they suffered caused them to make a doleful cry which brought five or six dozen of the same kind to them and by that means I was able to take nearly the whole of them."

Nearly a century after the Portugese, the Dutch came to Mauritius in 1598 to continue the destruction of the species. Again, the birds were used as a ready supply of fresh food for the sailors, with reports of forty or fifty of these large birds being taken aboard the ships in a single day.

DAVID DAY   However, it was not just the sailors who destroyed the Dodos. As the ships arrived they brought with them rats, dogs, cats, pigs and even monkeys. Over the years, more and more of these invading animals were left behind and bred on the island. At one point, the rat population of Mauritius was so great that the entire human population was forced to flee the island. Another time, the imported pigs were causing so much damage to the forests and farms that the human inhabitants of the island organized a hunt in which 1,500 wild pigs were killed in a single day.

The threat to the Dodos was increasing: their nests, built on the ground, left their eggs within easy reach of all the newly intro- duced predators. The defenceless chicks were easy prey for the cats and rats. Even the large adult birds were killed as the dogs hunted them out — unable to fly, they could not escape. By 1680, the Mauritian Dodo was extinct.

That, however, is not quite the end of the story of the Dodo. Few people realize there were once three other distinct Dodo species. One was an animal that was rather like an albino form which was simply called the White Dodo (*Victorionis imperialis*), and the other two were more distant cousins, called the Réunion Solitaire (*Ornithaptera soli- tarius*) and the Rodriguez Solitaire (*Pezohaps solitarius*).

The White Dodo lived in the more remote and mountainous regions of neighbouring Réunion, and consequently outlived the Mauritian Dodo by ninety years. It did not become extinct until 1770. The two Dodo relatives called Solitaires were of a similar size to the Dodos, but were never considered stupid, ugly or awkward ani- mals. In fact, they were described as being rather elegant, swan-like birds capable of considerable speed who, if need be, could become aggressive in defence of themselves or their young. These features notwithstanding, the Réunion Solitaire became extinct in 1700, while the Rodriguez Solitaire lasted out until 1800. Interestingly enough, it appears that several Dodos of various species were sent as live specimens to a number of European collectors. It is a great tragedy that these birds were not sufficiently important to be bred in captivity. Instead, they were displayed as mere curiosities. Had the collectors who received them tried to do so, they might still be with us. However doomed they were in their natural habitat, it would surely have been possible to keep them safely in zoos or parks. That the Dodos managed to survive the long, arduous sea journey that brought them to Europe indicated that they were tough, hardy creatures. From all accounts they adapted well to their new circumstances and there is nothing to indicate that they were not able to breed in captivity.

There is one poignant record of a Dodo being exhibited in London in 1638. Sir Hammon Lestrange saw a poster advertising this strange bird and went to see it for himself. He wrote later that he saw a huge bird, bigger than a turkey, which the keeper referred to as a Dodo. The keeper was at pains to point out the food of the Dodo, which was simply a pile of large stones in the corner of the bird's enclosure. Dodos certainly did eat a few pebbles, holding them in their gizzards to crush their food with; but the picture of that one lonely Dodo, confined to a small cage in a dark London house thousands of miles away from the sunny Mascarenes, being fed from a heap of stones and surrounded all day by hordes of curious people, is a sad one.

So, what lesson can we learn from the Dodo's extinction?

It is undoubtedly true that certain biological characteristics and geographical circumstances make some species more susceptible to extinction than others. But the sudden invasion and exploitation of the Mascarene Islands was so ruthless and extreme, it is ridiculous to blame the Dodo for its inability to adapt. Adaptability, speed, intelligence, and the ability to fight, fly or flee from enemies, were found in many of the animals who now share the fate of the Dodo. Some of the world's most numerous and superbly 'fit' species have been obliterated just as quickly as the Dodo.

On the Mascarene Islands, in particular, the Dodo's story was far from unique. No less than twenty-eight species — Dodos, tortoises, owls, starlings, parrots, rails, lizards and snakes — have become extinct in this island paradise. Today, over 80 per cent of the island's wildlife species are either critically endangered or extinct.

So, it must be said, beyond everything else, there is one lesson we must learn from the Dodo's extinction, and that lesson is exactly the opposite of the one implied in that little "fable of the Dodo" with which we began this chapter.

DAVID DAY   The single most important acknowledgement we must make is: since the Dodo, the survival or extinction of species has NOT been determined by the laws of nature. It has been determined by the laws, economics, politics and fashions or simple whims of the human race.

Forgive My Guilt

ROBERT P. TRISTRAM COFFIN

Not always sure what things called sins may be,
I am sure of one sin I have done.
It was years ago, and I was a boy,
I lay in the frostflowers with a gun,
The air ran blue as the flowers, I held my breath,
Two birds on golden legs slim as dream things
Ran like quicksilver on the golden sand,
My gun went off, they ran with broken wings
Into the sea, I ran to fetch them in,
But they swam with their heads high out to sea,
They cried like two sorrowful high flutes,
With jagged ivory bones where wings should be.

For days I heard them when I walked that headland
Crying out to their kind in the blue,
The other plovers were going over south
On silver wings leaving these broken two.
The cries went out one day, but I still hear them
Over all the sounds of sorrow in war or peace
I ever have heard, time cannot drown them.
Those slender flutes of sorrow never cease.
Two airy things forever denied the air!
I never knew how their lives at last were split,
But I have hoped for years all that is wild,
Airy, and beautiful will forgive my guilt.

Coyote Pup
Meets the Crazy People
in Kootenay National Park

DALE ZIEROTH

Brian brought him in
dumped in the back of his warden's truck and we watched him
die, a gasp at a time
spaced so far apart we knew he was
gone but suggested this or that anyway,
his breath hooked on a bone in his lungs,
his brown sides heaving for the sky
and we all felt for him in our different ways
which are the differences between men.
And twice Larry said, "Poor little fellow."
And Brian: "I could give him a shot of 'nectine
or a bullet but all I've got
is the .270 and that's
too big." So we hung on
till Ian pushed down on his ribs:
"Not much there." And still we
wanted him to run like the wind for the bush.
"Is that it?" I asked, hearing his
last lunge at the air, which it was, anyone
could tell he was gone,
off in a new direction
heading out somewhere else and leaving all
or nothing behind in those damn yellow eyes
staring out at me, out into a darkening world
where four men shuffled and laughed,
went in for coffee.

Inside with the rest of the crazy people
sitting down for coffee,
making words do all the work, talking shop, talking
park in the jargon of the civil servant man,
we know what chairs to sit in

we listen to the whirl of tongues
and the talk goes wildlife and telex and
choppers it goes numbers and man-years and
stats it goes nuts for
fifteen minutes
and behind the words sometimes we hear
the anger and sometimes we hear the pettiness
and then the hurt. And someone tries to tell me
what this park really needs
what this park is really like, but I know already
it's like a dead coyote pup
lying out in the back of a warden's truck
waiting for the plastic bag we're
going to stuff him in and then we're going to
shove him in the freezer along with
the lamb that got it from the logging truck
along with a half dozen favourite
birds wiped out by cars, specimens now
and we'll save you that way, fella
we'll cut off your head and throw it
up on the roof and wait till the bugs
clean you up and someday your skull will be
passed around
hand to human hand
and not one of them will be
afraid of you not one of them will let himself know
how the last gasp was also like a sigh
how it was the wrong way to die in the back of
a warden's truck looking at steel
watched by humans handled and pitied and
down on your side in the muck
a pup seven months out of the den.

Coffee's over we turn from our chairs
notice the blue sky outside
and cold sweet air that comes from the breath
of the animals and we hurry to our places
the crazy people and me, we gotta get back to our
paper work.

A SUNRISE ON THE VELD

DORIS LESSING

Every night that winter he said aloud into the dark of the pillow: Half past four! Half past four! Then he fell asleep at once, as if a shutter had fallen, and lay with his face turned to the clock so that he could see it first thing when he woke.

It was half past four to the minute, every morning. Triumphantly pressing down the alarm knob of the clock, which the dark half of his mind had outwitted, remaining vigilant all night and counting the hours as he lay relaxed in sleep, he huddled down for a last warm moment under the clothes, playing with the idea of lying abed for this once only. But he played with it for the fun of knowing that it was a weakness he could defeat without effort; just as he set the alarm each night for the delight of the moment when he woke and stretched his limbs, feeling the muscles tighten, and thought: Even my brain — even that! I can control every part of myself.

Luxury of warm rested body, with arms and legs and fingers waiting like soldiers for a word of command! Joy of knowing that the precious hours were given to sleep voluntarily! — for he had once stayed awake three nights running, to prove that he could, and then worked all day, refusing even to admit that he was tired; and now sleep seemed to him a servant to be commanded and refused.

The boy stretched his frame full-length, touching the wall at his head with his hands, and the bed foot with his toes; then he sprung out, like a fish leaping from water. And it was cold, cold.

He always dressed rapidly, so as to try and conserve his night-warmth till the sun rose two hours later; but by the time he had on his clothes his hands were numbed and he could scarcely hold his shoes. These he could not put on for fear of waking his parents, who never came to know how early he rose.

As soon as he stepped over the lintel, the flesh of his soles contracted on the chill earth, and his legs began to ache with cold. It was night: the stars were glittering, the trees standing black and still. He looked for signs of day, for the graying of the edges of a stone, or a lightening in the sky where the sun would rise, but there was nothing yet. Alert as an animal he crept past the dangerous window, standing poised with his hand on the sill for one proudly fastidious moment, looking in at the stuffy blackness of the room where his parents lay.

Feeling for the grass-edge of the path with his toes, he reached inside another window further along the wall, where his gun had been set in readiness the night before. The steel was icy, and numbed fingers slipped along it, so that he had to hold it in the crook of his arm for safety. Then he tiptoed to the room where the dogs slept, and was fearful that they might have been tempted to go before him; but they were waiting, their haunches crouched in reluctance at the cold, but ears and swinging tails greeting the sun ecstatically. His warning undertone kept them secret and silent till the house was a hundred yards back; then they bolted off into the bush, yelping excitedly. The boy imagined his parents turning in their beds and muttering: Those dogs again! before they were dragged back in sleep; and he smiled scornfully. He always looked back over his shoulder at the house before he passed a wall of trees that shut it from sight. It looked so low and small, crouching there under a tall and brilliant sky. Then he turned his back on it, and on the frowsting sleepers,[1] and forgot them.

He would have to hurry. Before the light grew strong he must be four miles away; and already a tint of green stood in the hollow of a leaf, and the air smelled of morning and the stars were dimming.

He slung the shoes over his shoulder, veld *skoen* that were crinkled and hard with the dews of a hundred mornings. They would be necessary when the ground became too hot to bear. Now he felt the chilled dust push up between his toes, and he let the muscles of his feet spread and settle into the shapes of the earth; and he thought: I could walk a hundred miles on feet like these! I could walk all day, and never tire!

He was walking swiftly through the dark tunnel of foliage that in daytime was a road. The dogs were invisibly ranging the lower travelways of the bush, and he heard them panting. Sometimes he felt a cold muzzle on his leg before they were off again, scouting for a trail to follow. They were not trained, but free-running companions of the hunt, who often tired of the long stalk before the final shots, and went off on their own pleasure. Soon he could see them, small and wild-looking in a wild strange light, now that the bush stood trembling on the verge of colour, waiting for the sun to paint earth and grass afresh.

The grass stood to his shoulders; and the trees were showering a faint silvery rain. He was soaked; his whole body was clenched in a steady shiver.

Once he bent to the road that was newly scored with animal trails, and regretfully straightened, reminding himself that the pleasure of tracking must wait till another day.

He began to run along the edge of a field, noting jerkily how it was filmed over with fresh spider web, so that the long reaches of great black clods seemed netted in glistening gray. He was using the steady lope he had learned by watching the natives, the run that is a dropping of the weight of the body from one foot to the next in a slow balancing movement that never tires, nor shortens the breath; and he felt the blood pulsing down his legs and along his arms, and the exultation and pride of body mounted in him till he was shutting his teeth hard against a violent desire to shout his triumph.

Soon he had left the cultivated part of the farm. Behind him the bush was low and black. In front was a long vlei, acres of long pale grass that sent back a hollowing gleam of light to a satiny sky. Near him thick swathes of grass were bent with the weight of water, and diamond drops sparkled on each frond.

The first bird woke at his feet and at once a flock of them sprang into the air, calling shrilly that day had come; and suddenly, behind him, the bush woke into song, and he could hear the guinea fowl calling far ahead of him. That meant they would now be sailing down from their trees into thick grass, and it was for them he had come: he was too late. But he did not mind. He forgot he had come to shoot. He set his legs wide, and balanced from foot to foot, and swung his gun up and down in both hands horizontally, in a kind of improvised exercise, and let his head sink back till it was pillowed in his neck muscles, and watched how above him small rosy clouds floated in a lake of gold.

Suddenly it all rose in him; it was unbearable. He leapt up into the air, shouting and yelling wild, unrecognizable noises. Then he began to run, not carefully, as he had before, but madly, like a wild thing. He was clean crazy, yelling mad with the joy of living and a superfluity of youth. He rushed down the vlei under a tumult of crimson and gold, while all the birds of the world sang about him. He ran in great leaping strides, and shouted as he ran, feeling his body rise into the crisp rushing air and fall back surely onto sure feet; and thought briefly, not believing that such a thing could happen to him, that he could break his ankle any moment, in this thick tangled grass. He cleared bushes like a duiker,[2] leapt over rocks, and finally came to a dead stop at a place where the ground fell abruptly away below him to the river. It had been a two-mile-long dash through the waist-high growth, and he was breathing hoarsely and could no longer sing. But he poised on a rock and looked down at stretches of water that gleamed through stooping trees, and thought suddenly: I am fifteen! Fifteen! The words came new to him, so that he kept repeating them wonderingly, with swelling excitement; and he felt the years of his life with his hands, as if he were counting marbles, each one hard and separate and compact, each one a wonderful shining thing. That was what he was: fifteen years of this rich soil, and this slow-moving water, and air that smelt like a challenge whether it was warm and sultry at noon, or as brisk as cold water, like it was now.

There was nothing he couldn't do, nothing! A vision came to him, as he stood there, like when a child hears the word *eternity* and tries to understand it, and time takes possession of the mind. He felt his life ahead of him as a great and wonderful thing, something that was his; and he said aloud, with the blood rising to his head: All the great men of the world have been as I am now, and there is nothing I can't become, nothing I can't do; there is no country in the world I cannot make part of myself, if I choose. I contain the world. I can make of it what I want. If I choose, I can change everything that is going to happen: it depends on me, and what I decide now.

The urgency and the truth and the courage of what his voice was saying exulted him so that he began to sing again, at the top of his voice, and the sound went echoing down the river gorge. He stopped for the echo, and sang again; stopped and shouted. That was what he was! — he sang, if he chose; and the world had to answer him.

And for minutes he stood there, shouting and singing and waiting for the lovely eddying sound of the echo; so that his own new strong thoughts came back and washed round his head, as if someone were answering him and encouraging him; till the gorge was full of soft voices clashing back and forth from rock to rock over the river. And then it seemed as if there was a new voice. He listened, puzzled, for it was not his own. Soon he was leaning forward, all his nerves alert, quite still: somewhere close to him there was a noise that was no joyful bird, nor tinkle of falling water, nor ponderous movement of cattle.

There it was again. In the deep morning hush that held his future and his past, was a sound of pain, and repeated over and over: it was a kind of shortened scream, as if someone, something, had no breath to scream. He came to himself, looked about him, and called for the dogs. They did not appear: they had gone off on their own business, and he was alone. Now he was clean sober, all the madness gone. His heart beating fast, because of that frightened screaming, he stepped carefully off the rock and went towards a belt of trees. He was moving cautiously, for not so long ago he had seen a leopard in just this spot.

At the edge of the trees he stopped and peered, holding his gun ready; he advanced, looking steadily about him, his eyes narrowed. Then all at once, in the middle of a step, he faltered, and his face was puzzled. He shook his head impatiently, as if he doubted his own sight.

There, between two trees, against a background of gaunt black rocks, was a figure from a dream, a strange beast that was horned and drunken-legged, but like something he had never even imagined. It seemed to be ragged. It looked like a small buck that had black ragged tufts of fur standing up irregularly all over it, with patches of raw flesh beneath . . . but the patches of rawness were disappearing under moving black and came again elsewhere; and all the time the creature screamed, in small gasping screams, and leaped drunkenly from side to side as if it were blind.

Then the boy understood: it *was* a buck. He ran closer, and again stood still, stopped by a new fear. Around him the grass was whispering and alive. He looked wildly about, and then down. The ground was black with ants, great energetic ants that took no notice of him, but hurried and scurried towards the fighting shape, like a glistening black water flowing through the grass.

And, as he drew in his breath and pity and terror seized him, the beast fell and the screaming stopped. Now he could hear nothing but one bird singing, and the sound of the rustling, whispering ants.

He peered over at the writhing blackness that jerked convulsively with the jerking nerves. It grew quieter. There were small twitches from the mass that still looked vaguely like the shape of a small animal.

It came into his mind that he should shoot it and end its pain; and he raised the gun. Then he lowered it again. The buck could no longer feel; its fighting was a mechanical protest of the nerves. But it was not that which made him put down the gun. It was a swelling feeling of rage and misery and protest that expressed itself in the thought: If I had not come it would have died like this; so why should I interfere? All over the bush things like this happen; they happen all the time; this is how life goes on, by living things dying in anguish. He gripped the gun between his knees and felt in his own limbs the myriad swarming pain of the twitching animal that could no longer feel, and set his teeth, and said over and over again under his breath: I can't stop it. I can't stop it. There is nothing I can do.

He was glad that the buck was unconscious and had gone past suffering, so that he did not have to make a decision to kill it even when he was feeling with his whole body: This is what happens, this is how things work.

It was right — that was what he was feeling. *It was right and nothing could alter it.*

The knowledge of fatality, of what has to be, had gripped him and for the first time in his life; and he was left unable to make any movements of brain or body, except to say: "Yes, yes. That is what living is." It had entered his flesh and his bones and grown into the furthest corners of his brain and would never leave him. And at that moment he could not have performed the smallest action of mercy, knowing as he did, having lived on it all his life, the vast, unalterable, cruel veld, where at any moment one might stumble over a skull or crush the skeleton of some small creature.

Suffering, sick, and angry, but also grimly satisfied with his new stoicism, he stood there leaning on his rifle, and watched the seething black mound grow smaller. At his feet, now, were ants trickling back with pink fragments in their mouths, and there was a fresh acid smell in his nostrils. He sternly controlled the uselessly convulsing muscles of his empty stomach, and reminded himself: The ants must eat too! At the same time he found that the tears were streaming down his face, and his clothes were soaked with the sweat of that other creature's pain.

The shape had grown small. Now it looked like nothing recognizable. He did not know how long it was before he saw the blackness thin, and bits of white showed through, shining in the sun — yes, there was the sun, just up, glowing over the rocks. Why, the whole thing could not have taken longer than a few minutes.

He began to swear, as if the shortness of the time was in itself unbearable, using the words he had heard his father say. He strode forward, crushing ants with each step, and brushing them off his clothes, till he stood above the skeleton, which lay sprawled under a small bush. It was clean-picked. It might have been lying there years, save that on the white bone were pink fragments of gristle. About the bones ants were ebbing away, their pincers full of meat.

The boy looked at them, big black ugly insects. A few were standing and gazing up at him with small glittering eyes.

"Go away!" he said to the ants, very coldly. "I am not for you — not just yet, at any rate. Go away." And he fancied that the ants turned and went away.

He bent over the bones and touched the sockets in the skull; that was where the eyes were, he thought incredulously, remembering the liquid dark eyes of a buck. And then he bent the slim foreleg bone, swinging it horizontally in his palm.

That morning, perhaps an hour ago, this small creature had been stepping proud and free through the bush, feeling the chill on its hide even as he himself had done, exhilarated by it. Proudly stepping the earth, tossing it horns, frisking a pretty white tail, it had sniffed the cold morning air. Walking like kings and conquerors it had moved through this free-held bush, where each blade of grass grew for it alone, and where the river ran pure sparkling water for its slaking.

And then — what had happened? Such a swift, sure-footed thing could surely not be trapped by a swarm of ants?

The boy bent curiously to the skeleton. Then he saw that the back leg that lay uppermost and strained out in the tension of death, was snapped midway in the thigh, so that broken bones jutted over each other uselessly. So that was it! Limping into the ant-masses it could not escape, once it had sensed the danger. Yes, but how had the leg been broken? Had it fallen, perhaps? Impossible, a buck was too light and graceful. Had some jealous rival horned it?

What could possibly have happened? Perhaps some Africans had thrown stones at it, as they do, trying to kill it for meat, and had broken its leg. Yes, that must be it.

Even as he imagined the crowd of running, shouting natives, and the flying stones, and the leaping buck, another picture came into his mind. He saw himself, on any one of these bright ringing mornings, drunk with excitement, taking a snapshot at some half-seen buck. He saw himself with the gun lowered, wondering whether he had missed or not, and thinking at last that it was late, and he wanted his breakfast, and it was not worthwhile to track miles after an animal that would very likely get away from him in any case.

For a moment he would not face it. He was a small boy again, kicking sulkily at the skeleton, hanging his head, refusing to accept responsibility. Then he straightened up, and looked down at the bones with an odd expression of dismay, all the anger gone out of him. His mind went quite empty; all around him he could see trickles of ants disappearing into the grass. The whispering noise was faint and dry, like the rustling of a cast snakeskin.

At last he picked up his gun and walked homewards. He was telling himself half defiantly that he wanted his breakfast. He was telling himself that it was getting very hot. Much too hot to be out roaming the bush.

Really, he was tired. He walked heavily, not looking where

A SUNRISE ON THE VELD

DORIS LESSING   he put his feet. When he came within sight of his home he stopped, knitting his brows. There was something he had to think out. The death of that small animal was a thing that concerned him, and he was by no means finished with it. It lay at the back of his mind uncomfortably.

Soon, the very next morning, he would get clear of everybody and go to the bush and think about it.

1. *frowsting sleepers:* people sleeping in a stuffy, musty room

2. *duiker:* kind of antelope

WINGS
OF A WILD GOOSE

CHRYSTOS

for Dian Million

A hen, one who could have brought more geese, a female,
                                        a wild one
dead   Shot by an excited ignorant young blond boy, his first
His mother threw the wings in the garbage   I rinsed them
brought them home, hung them spread wide on my studio wall
A reminder of so much, saving what I can't bear to be wasted
Wings
I dream of wings which carry me far above human bitterness
human walls   A goose who will have no more tiny pale fluttering
goslings to bring alive   to shelter   to feed   to watch fly
off on new wings   different winds
He has a lawn this boy   A pretty face which was recently paid
thousands of dollars to be in a television commercial   I clean
their house every Wednesday morning
2 dogs which no one brushes   flying hair everywhere
A black rabbit who is almost always out of
water   usually in a filthy cage   I've cleaned the cage
out of sympathy a few times although it is not part of what
are called my duties   I check the water as soon as I arrive
This rabbit & those dogs are the boy's pets   He is very lazy
He watches television constantly leaving the sofa in the den
littered with food wrappers, soda cans, empty cereal bowls
If I'm still there when he comes home, he is rude to me   If he
has his friends with him, he makes fun of me behind my back

CHRYSTOS

I muse on how he will always think of the woods
as an exciting place to kill   This family of three lives
on a five acre farm   They raise no crops   not even their own
vegetables or animals for slaughter   His father is a neurosurgeon
who longs to be a poet   His mother frantically searches
for christian enlightenment   I'm sad for her   though I don't like
her   because I know she won't find any   The boy does nothing
around the house without being paid   I'm 38 & still
haven't saved the amount of money he has in a passbook found
in the pillows of the couch under gum wrappers   That dead goose
This boy will probably never understand that it is not right
to take without giving   He doesn't know how to give   His mother
who cleaned & cooked the goose says she doesn't really like
to do it but can't understand why she should feel any different
about the goose than a chicken or hamburger from the
                                        supermarket
I bite my tongue & nod   I could explain to her that meat raised
for slaughter is very different than meat taken from the woods
where so few wild beings survive   That her ancestors are
responsible for the emptiness of this land   That lawns feed no
one   that fallow land lined with fences is sinful   That hungry
people need the food they could be growing   That spirituality
is not separate from food or wildness or respect or giving
But she already doesn't like me   because she suspects me
of reading her husband's poetry books when no one is around
& she's right   I do   I need the 32 dollars a week tolerating
them provides me   I wait for the wings on my wall to speak to me
guide my hungers   teach me winds I can't reach   I keep
these wings because walls are so hard   wildness so rare   because
ignorance must be remembered   because I am female because
                                        I fly

only in my dreams   because I too
will have no young to let go

THE DARK ONES

RICHARD CHRISTIAN MATHESON

"We have met the villains—"

The pain hadn't stopped for hours.

It seared his shoulder, and moving was making it worse. He shuddered, barely able to go on.

Only an hour ago.

The family had been together, the children playing in their favourite hiding place. Beautiful children, children of their own. The two of them had watched so proudly. They were lucky. Children were rare these days. And after her first terror with the Dark Ones, having a family had seemed impossible.

It was getting bad again.

What did they use that made their spears hurt so much? He'd felt it splay the skin when it buried itself in his back. It was like no pain he'd ever felt.

She and the children had escaped. He wasn't sure where. North, perhaps. Away from where the Dark Ones could try and murder them.

He knew the children must be tired, wherever they were. To be chased by the Dark Ones would be a nightmare for them.

He, too, was tired. But he knew he had to keep moving.

Night.

His eyes ached. He couldn't see far ahead. The Dark Ones might turn back. He knew they were frightened of the blackness. It could be his chance.

He stopped to breathe for a moment, and the cooling air soothed inside.

But seconds later, he screamed.

The Dark Ones had shot again. The thing was twisting in

his neck, and he shrieked for it to stop. He felt as if he were going to lose consciousness as it tore and burned inside.

She and the children.

He had to keep moving and see them once more. He loved them so. He had to get to them before the Dark Ones found him. *Keep moving*, he told himself.

Keep moving.

But the pain was spreading.

He looked back and saw the Dark Ones coming closer, shouting with glee. He couldn't breathe. *I'm growing weaker*, he realized. *Slowing down.*

He began to cry. He didn't want to die without seeing her and the children one last time. But the pain was getting worse.

He pleaded for someone to help.

Then, suddenly, he felt it: a rupturing explosion in his shoulder, and everything went blank.

A thick rain fell as the laughing voices neared and circled slowly, looking at what they had done.

The body had been ripped and shredded and oily blood splashed everywhere, dyeing everything it touched.

As they worked, joking among themselves, they didn't notice her watching.

With the children there beside her, she saw them haul her mate upward and began to weep. Then, moaning a cry of eternal loss which sprang to the depths, she and the children plunged their great bodies back into the bloody sea.

As they fled, seeking the safety of deeper waters, the echoes of their cries were answered by the haunted, faraway responses of the few who remained.

THE DREAMS
OF FISHKIND

KIT GARBETT

He was very smart, for a fish. Not as smart as the dolphin, or even the octopus. He certainly couldn't construct cities where fish work, or towns where fish sleep, or cars for fish to rush between towns and cities, or mortgages, or riots, or jobs. Not that smart; but for a fish he was smart.

He lived in the middle of the ocean, mid-way between the surface and the floor, a middle-of-the-road fish. If the fictitious pollsters were to ask his politics he would say centre right... with left leanings, very much a wet. A floating voter.

He saw neither surface nor ocean bed. Philosophically he sometimes wondered if there was an ocean surface; if so what lay beyond that surface? Then the terror of infinity gripped him, and he would think about something else, fearing for his sanity. The surface hovered on the border of existence, a speculation, not even a concept. The sun, the sky, the clouds, and whatever lies beyond, did not exist at all.

He had never seen land. He saw nothing that was not sea, or of the sea. In the shadowy depths, in the sea, there are no landmarks, no fixed points, no left, right, up or down. Things swam unexpectedly into view. Equally unexpectedly the lucky ones swam out.

There was a simple rule. Eat small things, flee big things. It made life easy. Things appeared and disappeared. Eat or flee. No need for jobs, riots, cars, and estate agents. It took little thought and gave time for philosophy.

It also gave freedom to travel, in all dimensions, as far as he wished in any direction. An ocean universe with no boundaries or restrictions. A limitless, yet limited world.

He knew spawning time, turbulent water, the earth's magnetic field, the electrical impulses of living creatures, and the true Being

KIT GARBETT of fishness. He knew this without qualifications, computers, papers, writers, or publishers. He was a very smart fish.

Then something different entered his world. It stretched across his world. It stayed there. This had never happened before. He pondered this. Because it was still there, he wondered if it had always been there, or always would be there. A dim glimmering of time entered his fishy mind.

He swam away until it was out of sight. He turned a half circle without navigation aids, charts, plans, committee decisions, or prior approval — and swam back. The thing reappeared. He tried this repeatedly, in different directions. Each time the thing reappeared.

He grew excited. If it was always there he could calculate how long it took to swim away and back to it. This could be useful. He could work at this "how long things took;" it held promise for him and for Fishkind.

He could swim away from and back to it, given the right direction. This he thought was getting somewhere. He had a direction in life. Somewhere to go to and from and he could tell how long he had been away. He paused to digest this and gobbled a shrimp, which also needed digesting.

The thing gave him much to think about and had opened up so much life. Could there be more of it? That was a revelation, that there could be more than swimming aimlessly and philosophizing.

He followed the thing down. It was a line he had to follow.

It stopped. It was finite. Where it stopped it changed form. There was something hard, and shiny, that caught the faint light. The thing gleamed in the darkness. Now it held wonder. It had opened his mind to new horizons and it reflected the light, giving illumination. This thing (he would name it later) held great potential.

On the hard shiny part there was a worm. A tasty-looking worm. Such a worm that a fish met only once. A worm that no fish could ignore. The most magnificent of all the thing's gifts.

This was what Fishkind wanted. This thing could offer so much. Mental stimulation, entertainment, aesthetic pleasure, and above all, material satisfaction and free worms for all. All Fishkind's dreams which hadn't previously existed — could be satisfied if it possessed the secret of the thing. And the thing was his to take. Only seize the moment, and grasp what had come into his life.

Strong, smart, fish lips closed around the worm. In seizing his Grail, he was transported. The power of the thing uplifted. Power such that even when he let go it still supported him. He rose through the water, rose till he thought his heart would burst.

He broke through. His watery world fell away. He was bathed in dazzling light. Light so intense that his eyes could scarcely stand it. He grasped in awe at the light. The light revealed many colours, splendid unimaginable colours. He gasped in amazement at the colours. Below him stretched the ocean, above him stretched the blue of a greater ocean. Instantly he realized the smallness of his world. He gasped in wonder at the immensity of the world.

Breathless he swung 'twixt Earth and Heaven and gasped at the revelation.

He gasped again.

Then he gasped no more.

The fisher was pleased with his catch. He had enough fish to feed his family. Now he took more to sell at the market. With money maybe he would someday buy a television, or car, or one of the other bright shiny things that the Western tourists had.

These things could offer so much. Mental stimulation, entertainment, aesthetic pleasure and, above all, material satisfaction. All his dreams could be satisfied if he only could possess these things. And the things could be his to take. Only seize the moment, and grasp what had come into his life.

The hook was baited again.

SOUND
of Thunder

RAY BRADBURY

The sign on the wall seemed to quaver under the film of sliding warm water. Eckels felt his eyelids blink over his stare, and the sign burned in this momentary darkness:

> TIME SAFARI, INC.
> SAFARIS TO ANY YEAR IN THE PAST.
> YOU NAME THE ANIMAL.
> WE TAKE YOU THERE.
> YOU SHOOT IT.

A warm phlegm gathered in Eckels' throat; he swallowed and pushed it down. The muscles around his mouth formed a smile as he put his hand slowly out upon the air, and in that hand waved a check for ten thousand dollars to the man behind the desk.

"Does this safari guarantee I come back alive?"

"We guarantee nothing," said the official, "except the dinosaurs." He turned. "This is Mr. Travis, your Safari Guide in the past. He'll tell you what and where to shoot. If he says no shooting, no shooting. If you disobey instructions, there's a stiff penalty of another ten thousand dollars, plus possible government action, on your return."

Eckels glanced across the vast office at a mass and tangle, a snaking and humming of wires and steel boxes, at an aurora that flickered now orange, now silver, now blue. There was a sound like a gigantic bonfire burning all of Time, all the years and all the parchment calendars, all the hours piled high and set aflame.

A touch of the hand and this burning would, on the instant, beautifully reverse itself. Eckels remembered the wording in the advertisements to the letter. Out of chars and ashes, out of dust and coals, like golden salamanders, the old years, the green years, might leap; roses sweeten the air, white hair turn Irish-black, wrinkles vanish; all, everything fly back to seed, flee death, rush down to their beginnings, suns rise in western skies and set in glorious easts, moons eat themselves opposite to the custom, all and everything cupping one in another like Chinese boxes, rabbits in hats, all and everything returning to the fresh death, the seed death, the green death, to the time before the beginning. A touch of a hand might do it, the merest touch of a hand.

"Hell and damn," Eckels breathed, the light of the Machine on his thin face. "A real Time Machine." He shook his head. "Makes you think. If the election had gone badly yesterday, I might be here now running away from the results. Thank God Keith won. He'll make a fine President of the United States."

"Yes," said the man behind the desk. "We're lucky. If Deutscher had gotten in, we'd have the worst kind of dictatorship. There's an anti-everything man for you, a militarist, anti-Christ, anti-human, anti-intellectual. People called us up, you know, joking but not joking. Said if Deutscher became President they wanted to go live in 1492. Of course it's not our business to conduct Escapes, but to form Safaris. Anyway, Keith's President now. All you got to worry about is—"

"Shooting my dinosaur," Eckels finished it for him.

"A *Tyrannosaurus rex*.... The Thunder Lizard, the damnedest monster in history. Sign the release. Anything happens to you, we're not responsible. Those dinosaurs are hungry."

Eckels flushed angrily. "Try to scare me!"

"Frankly, yes. We don't want anyone going who'll panic at the first shot. Six Safari leaders were killed last year, and a dozen hunters. We're here to give you the damnedest thrill a *real* hunter ever asked for. Travelling you back sixty million years to bag the biggest damned game in all Time. Your personal check's still there. Tear it up."

Mr. Eckels looked at the check for a long time. His fingers twitched.

RAY BRADBURY   "Good luck," said the man behind the desk. "Mr. Travis, he's all yours."

They moved silently across the room, taking their guns with them, toward the Machine, toward the silver metal and the roaring light.

First a day and then a night and then a day and then a night, then it was day-night-day-night-day. A week, a month, a year, a decade! A.D. 2055. A.D. 2019. 1999! 1957! Gone! The Machine roared.

They put on their oxygen helmets and tested the intercoms.

Eckels swayed on the padded seat, his face pale, his jaw stiff. He felt the trembling in his arms and he looked down and found his hands tight on the new rifle. There were four other men in the Machine. Travis, the Safari Leader, his assistant, Lesperance, and two other hunters, Billings and Kramer. They sat looking at each other, and the years blazed around them.

"Can these guns get a dinosaur cold?" Eckels felt his mouth saying.

"If you hit them right," said Travis on the helmet radio. "Some dinosaurs have two brains, one in the head, another far down the spinal column. We stay away from those. That's stretching luck. Put your first two shots into the eyes, if you can, blind them, and go back into the brain."

The Machine howled. Time was a film run backward. Suns fled and ten million moons fled after them. "Good God," said Eckels. "Every hunter that ever lived would envy us today. This makes Africa seem like Illinois."

The Machine slowed; its scream fell to a murmur. The Machine stopped.

The sun stopped in the sky.

The fog that had enveloped the Machine blew away and they were in old time, a very old time indeed, three hunters and two Safari Heads with their blue metal guns across their knees.

"Christ isn't born yet," said Travis. "Moses has not gone to the mountain to talk with God. The Pyramids are still in the earth, waiting to be cut up and put up. Remember that, Alexander, Caesar, Napoleon, Hitler — none of them exists."

The men nodded.

"That" — Mr. Travis pointed — "is the jungle of sixty million two thousand and fifty five years before President Keith."

He indicated a metal path that struck off into green wilderness, over steaming swamp, among giant ferns and palms.

"And that," he said, "is the Path, laid by Time Safari for your use. It floats six inches above the earth. Doesn't touch so much as one grass blade, flower, or tree. It's an antigravity metal. Its purpose is to keep you from touching this world of the past in any way. Stay on the path. Don't go off it. I repeat. *Don't go off.* For *any* reason! If you fall off, there's a penalty. And don't shoot any animal we don't okay."

"Why?" asked Eckels.

They sat in the ancient wilderness. Far birds' cries blew on a wind, and the smell of tar and an old salt sea, moist grasses, and flowers the colour of blood.

"We don't want to change the Future. We don't belong here in the Past. The government doesn't like us here. We have to pay big graft to keep our franchise. A Time Machine is damn finicky business. Not knowing it, we might kill an important animal, a small bird, a roach, a flower even, thus destroying an important link in a growing species."

"That's not clear," said Eckels.

"All right," Travis continued, "say we accidentally kill one mouse here. That means all the future families of this one particular mouse are destroyed, right?"

"Right."

"And all the families of the families of that one mouse! With a stamp of your foot, you annihilate first one, then a dozen, then a thousand, a million, a *billion* possible mice!"

"So they're dead," said Eckels. "So what?"

"So what?" Travis snorted quietly. "Well, what about the foxes that'll need those mice to survive? For want of ten mice, a fox dies. For want of ten foxes, a lion starves. For want of a lion, all manner of insects, vultures, infinite billions of life forms are thrown into chaos and destruction. Eventually it all boils down to this: fifty-nine million years later, a cave man, one of a dozen on the entire world, goes hunting wild boar or saber-tooth tiger for food. But you, friend, have stepped on all the tigers in that region. By stepping on one single mouse. So the cave man starves. And the cave man, please note, is not just any expendable man, no! He is an entire future nation. From his loins would have sprung ten children. From their loins one hundred children, and thus onward to a civilization. Destroy this one man, and you destroy a race, a people, an entire history of life. It is comparable to slaying some of Adam's grandchildren. The stomp of your foot, on one mouse, could start an earthquake, the effects of which could shake our earth and destinies down through Time, to their very foundations. With the death of that one cave man, a billion others yet unborn are throttled in the womb. Perhaps Rome never rises on its seven hills. Perhaps Europe is forever a dark forest, and only Asia waxes healthy and teeming. Step on a mouse and you crush the Pyramids. Step on a mouse and you leave your print, like a Grand Canyon, across Eternity. Queen Elizabeth might never be born, Washington might not cross the Delaware, there might ever be a United States at all. So be careful. Stay on the path. *Never* step off!"

"I see," said Eckels. "Then it wouldn't pay for us even to touch the *grass*?"

"Correct. Crushing certain plants could add up infinitesimally. A little error here would multiply in sixty million years, all out of proportion. Of course maybe our theory is wrong. Maybe Time can't be changed by us. Or maybe it can be changed only in little subtle ways. A dead mouse here makes an insect imbalance there, a population disproportion later, a bad harvest further on, a depression, mass starvation, and finally, a change in social temperament in far-flung countries. Something much more subtle, like that. Perhaps only a soft breath, a whisper, a hair, pollen on the air, such a slight, slight change that unless you looked close you wouldn't see it. Who knows? Who really can say he knows? We don't know. We're guessing. But until we do know for certain whether our messing around in Time can make a big roar or a little rustle in history, we're being damned careful. This Machine, this Path, your clothing and bodies, were sterilized, as you know, before the journey. We wear these oxygen helmets so we can't introduce our bacteria into an ancient atmosphere."

"How do we know which animals to shoot?"

"They're marked with red paint," said Travis. "Today, before our journey, we sent Lesperance here back with the Machine. He came to this particular era and followed certain animals."

"Studying them?"

"Right," said Lesperance. "I track them through their entire existence, noting which of them lives longest. Very few. How many times they mate. Not often. Life's short. When I find one that's going to die when a tree falls on him, or one that drowns in a tar pit, I note the exact hour, minute, and second. I shoot a paint bomb. It leaves a red patch on his hide. We can't miss it. Then I correlate our arrival in the Past so that we meet the Monster not more than two minutes before he would have died anyway. This way, we kill only animals with no future, that are never going to mate again. You see how careful we are?"

"But if you came back this morning in Time," said Eckels eagerly, "you must've bumped into us, our Safari! How did it turn out? Was it successful? Did all of us get through — alive?"

Travis and Lesperance gave each other a look.

"That'd be a paradox," said the latter. "Time doesn't permit that sort of mess — a man meeting himself. When such occasions threaten, Time steps aside. Like an airplane hitting an air pocket. You felt the Machine jump just before we stopped? That was us passing ourselves on the way back to the Future. We saw nothing. There's no way of telling if this expedition was a success, if we got our monster, or whether all of — meaning you, Mr. Eckels — got out alive."

Eckels smiled palely.

"Cut that," said Travis sharply. "Everyone on his feet!"

They were ready to leave the Machine.

The jungle was high and the jungle was broad and the jungle was the entire world forever and forever. Sounds like music and sounds like flying tents filled the sky, and those were pterodactyls soaring with cavernous gray wings, gigantic bats out of a delirium and a night fever. Eckels, balanced on the narrow Path, aimed his rifle playfully.

"Stop that!" said Travis. "Don't even aim for fun, damn it! If your gun should go off —"

Eckels flushed. "Where's our *Tyrannosaurus*?"

Lesperance checked his wrist watch. "Up ahead. We'll bisect

his trail in sixty seconds. Look for the red paint, for Christ's sake. Don't shoot till we give the word. Stay on the Path. *Stay on the Path!*"

They moved forward in the wind of morning.

"Strange," murmured Eckels. "Up ahead, sixty million years, Election Day over. Keith made President. Everyone celebrating. And here we are, a million years lost, and they don't exist. The things we worried about for months, a lifetime, not even born or thought about yet."

"Safety catches off, everyone!" ordered Travis. "You, first shot, Eckels. Second, Billings. Third, Kramer."

"I've hunted tiger, wild boar, buffalo, elephant, but Jesus, this is *it*," said Eckels. "I'm shaking like a kid."

"Ah," said Travis.

Everyone stopped.

Travis raised his hand. "Ahead," he whispered. "In the mist. There he is. There's His Royal Majesty now."

The jungle was wide and full of twitterings, rustling, murmurs, and sighs.

Suddenly it all ceased, as if someone had shut a door.

Silence.

A sound of thunder.

Out of the mist, one hundred yards away, came *Tyrannosaurus rex*.

"Jesus God," whispered Eckels.

"Sh!"

It came on great oiled, resilient, striding legs. It towered thirty feet above half of the trees, a great evil god, folding its delicate watchmaker's claws close to its oily reptilian chest. Each lower leg was a piston, a thousand pounds of white bone, sunk in thick ropes of muscle, sheathed over in a gleam of pebbled skin like the mail of a terrible warrior. Each thigh was a ton of meat, ivory, and steel mesh. And from the great breathing cage of the upper body those two delicate arms dangled out front, arms with hands which might pick up and examine men like toys, while the snake neck coiled. And the head itself, a ton of sculptured stone, lifted easily upon the sky. Its mouth gaped, exposing a fence of teeth like daggers. Its eyes rolled, ostrich eggs, empty of all expression save hunger. It closed its mouth in a death grin. It ran, its pelvic bones crushing aside trees and bushes, its taloned feet clawing damp earth, leaving prints six inches deep wherever it settled its weight. It ran with a gliding ballet step, far too poised and balanced for its ten tons. It moved in a sunlit arena warily, its beautifully reptile hands feeling the air.

"My God!" Eckels twitched his mouth. "It could reach up and grab the moon."

"Sh!" Travis jerked angrily. "He hasn't seen us yet."

"It can't be killed." Eckels pronounced this verdict quietly, as if there could be no argument. He had weighed the evidence and this was his considered opinion. The rifle in his hands seemed a cap gun. "We were fools to come. This is impossible."

"Shut up!" hissed Travis.

"Nightmare!"

"Turn around," commanded Travis. "Walk quietly to the machine. We'll remit one-half your fee."

"I didn't realize it would be this big," said Eckels. "I miscalculated, that's all. And now I want out."

"It sees us!"

"There's the red paint on its chest!"

The Thunder Lizard raised itself. Its armoured flesh glittered like a thousand green coins. The coins, crusted with slime, steamed. In the slime, tiny insects wriggled, so that the entire body seemed to twitch and undulate, even while the monster itself did not move. It exhaled. The stink of raw flesh blew down the wilderness.

"Get me out of here," said Eckels. "It was never like this before. I was always sure I'd come through alive. I had good guides, good safaris, and safety. This time, I figured wrong. I've met my match and admit it. This is too much for me to get hold of."

"Don't run," said Lesperance. "Turn around. Hide in the Machine."

"Yes." Eckels seemed to be numb. He looked at his feet as if trying to make them move. He gave a grunt of helplessness.

"Eckels!"

He took a few steps, blinking, shuffling.

"Not *that* way!"

RAY BRADBURY   The Monster, at the first motion, lunged forward with a terrible scream. It covered one hundred yards in four seconds. The rifles jerked up and blazed fire. A windstorm from the beast's mouth engulfed them in the stench of slime and old blood. The Monster roared, teeth glittering with sun.

Eckels, not looking back, walked blindly to the edge of the Path, his gun limp in his arms, stepped off the Path and walked, not knowing it, in the jungle. His feet sank into green moss. His legs moved him, and he felt alone and remote from the events behind.

The rifles cracked again. Their sound was lost in shriek and lizard thunder. The great lever of the reptile's tail swung up, lashed sideways. Trees exploded in clouds of leaf and branch. The Monster twitched its jeweller's hands down to fondle the men, to twist them in half, to crush them like berries, to cram them into its teeth and its screaming throat. Its boulder-stone eyes levelled with the men. They saw themselves mirrored. They fired at the metallic eyelids and the blazing black iris.

Like a stone idol, like a mountain avalanche, *Tyrannosaurus* fell. Thundering, it clutched trees, pulled them with it. It wrenched and tore the metal Path. The men flung themselves back and away. The body hit, ten tons of cold flesh and stone. The guns fired. The Monster lashed its armoured tail, twitched its snake jaws, and lay still. A fount of blood spurted from its throat. Somewhere inside, a sac of fluids burst. Sickening gushes drenched the hunters. They stood, red and glistening.

The thunder faded.

The jungle was silent. After the avalanche, a green peace. After the nightmare, morning.

Billings and Kramer sat on the pathway, and threw up. Travis and Lesperance stood with smoking rifles, cursing steadily.
In the Time Machine, on his face, Eckels lay shivering. He had found his way back to the Path, climbed into the Machine.
Travis came walking, glanced at Eckels, took cotton gauze from a metal box, and returned to the others, who were sitting on the Path.

"Clean up."

They wiped the blood from their helmets. They began to curse too. The Monster lay, a hill of solid flesh. Within, you could hear the sighs and murmurs as the furthest chambers of it died, the organs malfunctioning, liquids running a final instant from pocket to sac to spleen, everything shutting off, closing up forever. It was like standing by a wrecked locomotive or a steam shovel at quitting time, all valves being released or levered tight. Bones cracked; the tonnage of its own flesh, off balance, dead weight, snapped the delicate fore-arms, caught underneath. The meat settled, quivering.

Another cracking sound. Overhead, a gigantic tree branch broke from its heavy mooring, fell. It crashed upon the dead beast with finality.

"There." Lesperance checked his watch. "Right on time. That's the giant tree that was scheduled to fall and kill this animal originally." He glanced at the two hunters. "You want the trophy picture?"

"What?"

"We can't take a trophy back to the Future. The body has to stay right here where it would have died originally, so the insects, birds, and bacteria can get at it, as they were intended to. Everything in balance. The body stays. But we *can* take a picture of you standing near it."

The two men tried to think, but gave up, shaking their heads.

They let themselves be led along the metal Path. They sank wearily onto the Machine cushions. They gazed back at the ruined Monster, the stagnating mound, where already strange reptilian birds and golden insects were busy at the steaming armour.

A sound on the floor of the Time Machine stiffened them. Eckels sat there, shivering.

"I'm sorry," he said at last.

"Get up!" cried Travis.

Eckels got up.

"Go out on that Path alone," said Travis.

He had his rifle pointed. "You're not coming back in the Machine. We're leaving you here!"

Lesperance seized Travis' arm. "Wait —"

"Stay out of this!" Travis shook his hand away. "This son of a bitch nearly killed us. But it isn't *that* so much. Hell, no. It's his *shoes*! Look at them! He ran off the Path. My God, that *ruins* us! Christ knows how much we'll forfeit. Tens of thousands of dollars of

RAY BRADBURY   insurance! We guarantee no one leaves the Path. He left it. Oh, the damn fool! I'll have to report to the government. They might revoke our licence to travel. God knows what he's done to Time, to History!"

"Take it easy, all we did was kick up some dirt."

"How do we *know*?" cried Travis. "We don't know anything! It's all a damn mystery! Get out of there, Eckels!"

Eckels fumbled his shirt. "I'll pay anything. A hundred thousand dollars!"

Travis glared at Eckel's checkbook and spat. "Go out there. The Monster's next to the Path. Stick your arms up to your elbows in his mouth. Then you can come back with us."

"That's unreasonable!"

"The Monster's dead, you yellow bastard. The bullets! The bullets can't be left behind. They don't belong in the Past; they might change something. Here's my knife. Dig them out!"

The jungle was alive again, full of the old tremorings and bird cries. Eckels turned slowly to regard the primeval garbage dump, that hill of nightmares and terror. After a long time, like a sleepwalker, he shuffled out along the Path.

He returned, shuddering, five minutes later, his arms soaked and red to the elbows. He held out his hands. Each held a number of steel bullets. Then he fell. He lay where he fell, not moving.

"You didn't have to make him do that," said Lesperance.

"Didn't I? It's too early to tell." Travis nudged the still body. "He'll live. Next time he won't go hunting game like this. Okay." He jerked his thumb wearily at Lesperance. "Switch on. Let's go home."

1492. 1776. 1812.

They cleaned their hands and faces. They changed their caking shirts and pants. Eckels was up and around again, not speaking. Travis glared at him for a full ten minutes.

"Don't look at me," cried Eckels. "I haven't done anything."

"Who can tell?"

"Just ran off the Path, that's all, a little mud on my shoes — what do you want me to do — get down and pray?"

"We might need it. I'm warning you, Eckels, I might kill you yet. I've got my gun ready."

"I'm innocent. I've done nothing!"

1999. 2000. 2055.

The Machine stopped.

"Get out," said Travis.

The room was there as they had left it. But not the same as they had left it. The same man sat behind the same desk. But the same man did not quite sit behind the same desk.

Travis looked around swiftly, "Everything okay here?" he snapped.

"Fine. Welcome home!"

Travis did not relax. He seemed to be looking at the very atoms of the air itself, at the way the sun poured through the one high window.

"Okay, Eckels, get out. Don't ever come back."

Eckels could not move.

"You heard me," said Travis. "What're you *staring* at?"

Eckels stood smelling of the air, and there was a thing to the air, a chemical taint so subtle, so slight, that only a faint cry of his subliminal senses warmed him that it was there. The colours, white, gray, blue, orange, in the wall, in the furniture, in the sky beyond the window, were... were.... And there was a *feel*. His flesh twitched. His hands twitched. He stood drinking the oddness with the pores of his body. Somewhere, someone must have been screaming one of those whistles that only a dog can hear. His body screamed silence in return. Beyond this room, beyond this wall, beyond this man who was not quite the same man seated at this desk that was not quite the same desk... lay an entire world of streets and people. What sort of world it was now, there was no telling. He could feel them moving there, beyond the walls, almost like so many chess pieces blown in a dry wind....

But the immediate thing was the sign painted on the office wall, the same sign he had read earlier on first entering.

Somehow, the sign had changed.

TYME SAFARI INC.
SEFARIS TU ANY YEER EN THE PAST.
YU NAIM THE ANIMALL.
WE TAEK YOU THAIR.
YU SHOOT ITT.

Eckels felt himself fall into a chair. He fumbled crazily at the thick slime on his boots. He held up a clod of dirt, trembling. "No, it can't be. Not a little thing like that. No!"

Embedded in the mud, glistening green and gold and black, was a butterfly, very beautiful, and very dead.

"Not a little thing like *that!* Not a butterfly!" cried Eckels.

It fell to the floor, an exquisite thing, a small thing that could upset balances and knock down a line of small dominoes and then big dominoes and then gigantic dominoes, all down the years across Time. Eckels' mind whirled. It couldn't change things. Killing one butterfly couldn't be that important! Could it?

His face was cold. His mouth trembled, asking: "Who — who won the presidential election yesterday?"

The man behind the desk laughed. "You're joking? You know damn well. Deutscher, of course! Who else? Not that damn weakling Keith. We got an iron man now, a man with guts, by God!" The official stopped. "What's wrong?" Eckels moaned. He dropped to his knees. He scrabbled at the golden butterfly with shaking fingers. "Can't we," he pleaded to the world, to himself, to the officials, to the Machine, "can't we take it back, can't we make it alive again? Can't we start over? Can't we —"

He did not move. Eyes shut, he waited, shivering. He heard Travis breathe loud in the room; he heard Travis shift his rifle, click the safety catch, and raise the weapon.

There was a sound of thunder.

HARD QUESTIONS

MARGARET TSUDA

Why not mark the land
into neat rectangles
squares and clover leafs?

Put on them cubes of
varying sizes
according to use —
dwellings
        singles/multiples
complexes
        commercial/industrial.

Bale them together with
bands of roads.

What if a child shall cry
"I have never known spring!
I have never seen autumn!"

What if a man shall say
"I have never heard
silence fraught with living as
in swamp or forest!"
What if the eye shall never see
marsh bird and muskrats?

Does not the heart need
wilderness?
Does not the thought need
something
to rest upon
not self-made by man,
a bosom
not his own?

Just One Thing

THE LAKE

ISLE OF INNISFREE

WILLIAM BUTLER YEATS

I will arise and go now, and go to Innisfree,
And a small cabin build there, of clay and wattles[1] made:
Nine bean-rows will I have there, a hive for the honeybee,
And live alone in the bee-loud glade.

And I shall have some peace there, for peace comes dropping
    slow
Dropping from the veils of the morning to where the cricket sings;
There midnight's all a glimmer, and noon a purple glow,
And evening full of the linnet's wings.

I will arise and go now, for always night and day
I hear lake water lapping with low sounds by the shore;
While I stand on the roadway, or on the pavements grey,
I hear it in the deep heart's core.

1. Interlaced rods and twigs.

WHY WE CARE

let us tell

you some stories

CAL FUSSMAN

Set before the body was a can of chicken soup, a bottle of Pepto-Bismol and a box of Band-Aids. Get-well cards came from as far away as Japan and Australia, and there were poems from local first-graders. Scientists walked around and shook their heads. People dropped to their knees and prayed.

Maybe this was what it took. It was only now, after someone had poisoned the 600-year-old Treaty Oak in Austin Texas, that we finally found ourselves looking at a tree this way — as a living thing.

A man donated $100,000 to save it. The manufacturer of the potent herbicide that had been mysteriously poured around the roots offered a $10,000 reward for the capture of the tree's posioner. There was a massive search. A man was accused of doing the poisoning and jailed. In bars, people talked about hanging him from one of the Treaty Oak's limbs.

Why all the commotion, all the passion, over the possible loss of a single tree! Especially now — at the end of a decade in which cathedrals of fir and redwood had been levelled and sections of forests in Montana and Washington were made to look like they'd been given a haircut. Who mourned them! "Once you've seen one red-wood, you've seen them all," said Ronald Reagan, summing up the prevailing attitude of the '80s.

Even Earth Day, which first rang an environmental alarm 20

years ago, has become a day to *remember* when people protested the dumping of chemicals in Love Canal, not a day to *do* something.

But this Earth Day will be different, at least for me. When I step outside, I'll remember the yellow-green leaves on one side of the Treaty Oak and the leafless branches hanging limply on the other. If there are candy wrappers or crushed soda cans under the trees I pass, I will stop to pick them up. Yes, this April 22 will be different, and so will the day after and the day after that...

Maybe you, too, would stop to appreciate a tree on Earth Day, or any day, if you had sat with 98-year-old Dorothea Stegeman in Athens, Ga., and heard the story of her Olympic Tree. It was an oak sapling she had promised to take home to the University of Georgia for her friend Spec Towns. He had received it, along with a gold medal, for winning the 110-meter hurdles at the 1936 Olympic Games in Berlin.

Dorothea carried the sapling through Germany, Switzerland, France, and England, by car and train, across the ocean to America by boat, caring for it as if it were a child. She watched them plant it near the university's Memorial Hall, where it grew tall and mighty. She watched them move it behind the football stadium when Memorial Hall needed room to expand. And then, in 1966, when the stadium needed room to expand, she heard some people wanted to chop it down.

Dorothea's grandchildren and Spec's grandchildren were supposed to sit under that tree one sunny day and hear about how a boy who'd never run a race in high school received a scholarship to the university... how the sports editor of the local paper had seen him high jumping in a backyard and written an article about it... and how this boy had gone on to set a world record at the Olympics. And the grandchildren were supposed to pass the story on to *their* grandchildren under those same branches. That was the point of the sapling.

Dorothea fought and fought. And won. A maintenance crew was instructed to move the tree to a spot outside the university's coliseum.

And now in her living room, the words were tumbling faster and faster from Dorothea's lips: "It was twelve minutes to five o'clock when they discovered the hole they'd dug wasn't large enough for the tree. And the workmen wanted to go home. I was standing right there, watching. One of them just whacked the roots off one side of the tree to make it fit in the hole. So fast, there was no time to protest. Just *whacked* 'em right off."

A year later the tree turned black and died.

Maybe you too, would think about recycling paper on Earth Day, or any day, if you had met the woman who lay in a fetal position on the floor of an Oregon jail while inmates punched and kicked at her.

Karen Wood had not harmed anybody or damaged anybody's property. She was in jail because she had chained her neck to logging machinery with a bicycle lock to stop the cutting of old growth at the Sapphire sale in Siskiyou National Forest. For Karen, it is always twelve minutes to five o'clock.

There were five others with Karen. They called themselves the Sapphire Six. According to Karen, one of the loggers threatened to rape her. Then came the sheriff's men, the criminal mischief charge, the court appearance, the sentencing.

In the Curry County Jail, Karen said she tried to protect the black member of the Sapphire six when a brawl erupted and some of the inmates began to smash the woman's head against the bars. The inmates turned on Karen and dragged her toward the toilet bowl. She didn't know if they intending to smash her head against the porcelain or dunk it into the water. The guard came just as she was going to find out. When Karen and her friends were released, they had to go to civil court, where the logging company was awarded $30,000 in damages.

Karen is 28 years old. She makes little money as a part-time secretary in a law firm. Her parents don't understand her. She keeps on protesting, keeps on crying as she hears the trees fall, keeps going to jail.

Is it worth it?

"Have you ever heard of the Chipko women?" she asked. Years ago in India, she said, soldiers were ordered to cut down trees in certain villages to fuel an iron smelter. In one village the women hugged the trees in protest — and the soldiers sawed through them. "And do you know what! More would come to take their place. Because they knew if they didn't, there was no life without trees anyway."

Maybe you, too, would sit under a pine tree and feel your lungs swell with fresh air on Earth Day, or any day, if Joe Dickey had told you how as a boy he was knocked unconscious by a belch of gas from the copper-smelting plant in Copperhill, Tenn. "Didn't think much about it back them," he said. "That was thirty-five years ago. I just got up and went on home as if it was perfectly normal."

Later we drove past the smokestacks and into a red-clay desert, a 56-square-mile dust bowl that was once a forest. By the early years of this century, Joe said, all the trees were chopped down for fuel to roast copper ore. The pollution got so thick, mules had to wear bells to keep from bumping into each other. He told of how the sulfer dioxide released into the air stripped away all the area's remaining vegetation, how his father worked at the plant and died of lung cancer, and how cancer wasn't something workers talked much about during the '50s, when the living was good. Then times changed. The new owners planted more trees, but copper prices dropped and the layoffs began.

So now there were young pines struggling to reclaim the desert — but store windows in town were empty. And you couldn't help thinking that this was like a long and terrible war: Man wins, nature loses. Nature wins, man loses.

On my way out of town, I stopped to look at a young pine tree. A healing tree. They say that by inhaling the smoke of burning pine branches people were saved from the influenza epidemic that killed millions at the beginning of the century. I pulled off some needles and chewed the ends. There is more vitamin C in a single pine bough than in a crate of oranges.

Try to count all the things a tree can give and you'll be at it all day. Paper, oxygen, bananas, rubber, almonds, firewood, houses...

Mangrove roots gave Native Americans an anchor to lash their children to so they wouldn't be blown away during hurricanes. And the Angel Oak in South Carolina gave blacks and whites the one place were they could picnic together during the darkest days of segregation. The twig of a sweet birch gave Dee Smith in North Carolina a toothbrush when she was a little girl. And the Moreton Bay Fig Tree in Santa Barbara, Calif., gave homeless men a place to plant a mailbox in an effort to have an address and the right to vote.

The lullaby of wind rustling through the palm fronds in

CAL FUSSMAN   Miami Beach gives old people sleep. Yew trees, scientists are beginning to believe, may give the cure for cancer.

In Krakow, Mo., about an hour's ride west of St. Louis, there is a maple tree that Rocky Sickmann's mom and dad tied a yellow ribbon around as a gesture of hope during the 444 days their son was a hostage in Iran. In the living room of his folks' home, Rocky talked about how his memories of trees from boyhood were what sustained him when he sat staring into the corner of a room, his arms and legs tied to a chair. Memories of sledding over snow through an obstacle course of trees, bending wood in the backyard into a bow and arrow, of decorating the big maple tree out front with flashing Christmas lights. "Your family, your friends, your trees," he said. "You take for granted you'll always have them — until you don't."

Maybe you, too, would stop a moment on Earth Day, or any day, and wonder how many trees will be left for your great-grandchildren to climb if you'd seen the huge X marks spray-painted on the trees of Orcas Island off the coast of Washington.

Thousands of years ago the Lummi Indians lived on this island in harmony with the cedar, the fir, the madrona. The cedar gave them canoes, clam baskets and lines to pull in halibut and salmon, blankets and remedies, even a burial ground. The dead were placed with their possessions in cedar canoes between the forked branches of the trees on a point of the island called Ts'el-xwisen.

Then came white settlers, and a smallpox epidemic. The Lummis were moved to a reservation on the mainland. But many came back to visit the burial site, for it was sacred. And many of the island's new inhabitants loved to walk on the trail around the site, for it was peaceful, and sometimes one could find all the colors of the rainbow splashed in the bark of the madrona tree. The land came to be called Madrona Point, and it came to be owned by a developer who made plans to build a condominium on top of the burial ground.

The Lummis and island residents held demonstrations and vigils. The developer put chains around the area and armed guards in front of the chains. A spray-painted X marked the trees they would cut first.

And the chain saws would have gone to work if it hadn't been for William Randolph Hearst III, whose family's publishing empire was built on felled trees. He put his money and the weight of his name into the struggle. After years of discord, President George Bush approved a $2.2 million grant to buy back the burial ground.

In February island residents and Lummis embraced and cried as Hearst handed the deed to the Indians. On a sunny afternoon they all walked around Ts'el-xwisen. And from the woods a Lummi named Bill James watched the sun spangle off pure blue water that massaged the rocky shore. A white man approached. "It's great to know that I will always be able to come here," he said. "Thank you."

"Don't thank *me*," the Lummi replied. "It's not our land. It's everybody's land."

Maybe you, too, would consider planting a sapling on Earth Day, or any day, if you skied into 60 mph winds with the temperature at 20 below zero to try to see the world's oldest tree.

The Methuselah, it's called, a bristlecone pine that grows an inch every 100 years. When Jesus Christ was nailed to pieces of wood, when Buddha found Truth under branches, when the wooden horse was rolled into Troy, the Methuselah atop the White Mountains of California was enduring summers so dry they would swell a man's tongue and winters that could freeze off his fingers. Think of it: *Four thousand, seven hundred years old.*

You can go to Schulman Grove at Inyo National Forest, where it stands with the other ancient bristlecone pines, but the rangers will not tell you which one is *the* Methuselah. If people knew, they would peel off pieces for souvenirs, and they would trample the shallow root system. Then surely it would die.

The climb to 10,000 feet was exhausting. Finally, I skied up to one of the great-great-granddaddies. It looked like an old man, gnarled and wrinkled — but it felt like the cheek of a baby, polished by thousands of years of ice and wind. A few tufts of scrub brush and the bristlecone pines — that is about all that can exist up here. They survive by the miracle of sucking every trace of nutrient and moisture from the rocky soil. And the message they give is this: Do not take a single thing for granted.

Maybe you, too, will not take a single thing for granted on

CAL FUSSMAN   Earth Day, or any day, if you realize that we've been pulling on a rubber band that has no more to give, that is about to snap.

Maybe you, too, will realize it's our turn to give a little.

THE MAN
who planted
Trees

JEAN GIONO

For a human character to reveal truly exceptional qualities, one must have the good fortune to be able to observe its performance over many years. If this performance is devoid of all egoism, if its guiding motive is unparalleled generosity, if it is absolutely certain that there is no thought of recompense and that, in addition, it has left its visible mark upon the earth, then there can be no mistake.

About forty years ago I was taking a long trip on foot over mountain heights quite unknown to tourists, in that ancient region where the Alps thrust down into Provence. All this, at the time I embarked upon my long walk through these deserted regions, was barren and colourless land. Nothing grew there but wild lavendar.

     I was crossing the area at its widest point, and after three days' walking, found myself in the midst of unparalleled desolation. I camped near the vestiges of an abandoned village. I had run out of water the day before, and had to find some. These clustered houses, although in ruins, like an old wasps' nest, suggested that there must once have been a spring or well here. There was indeed a spring, but it was dry. The five or six houses, roofless, gnawed by wind and rain, the tiny chapel with its crumbling steeple, stood about like the houses and chapels in living villages, but all life had vanished.

     It was a fine June day, brilliant with sunlight, but over this unsheltered land, high in the sky, the wind blew with unendurable ferocity. It growled over the carcasses of the houses like a lion disturbed at its meal. I had to move my camp.

After five hours' walking I had still not found water and there was nothing to give me any hope of finding any. All about me was the same dryness, the same coarse grasses. I thought I glimpsed in the distance a small black silhouette, upright, and took it for the trunk of a solitary tree. In any case I started toward it. It was a shepherd. Thirty sheep were lying about him on the baking earth.

He gave me a drink from his water-gourd and, a little later, took me to his cottage in a fold of the plain. He drew his water — excellent water — from a very deep natural well above which he had constructed a primitive winch.

The man spoke little. This is the way of those who live alone, but one felt that he was sure of himself, and confident in his assurance. That was unexpected in this barren country. He lived, not in a cabin, but in a real house built of stone that bore plain evidence of how his own efforts had reclaimed the ruin he had found there on his arrival. His roof was strong and sound. The wind on its tiles made the sound of the sea upon its shore.

The place was in order, the dishes washed, the floor swept, his rifle oiled; his soup was boiling over the fire. I noticed then that he was cleanly shaved, that all his buttons were firmly sewed on, that his clothing had been mended with the meticulous care that makes the mending invisible. He shared his soup with me and afterwards, when I offered my tobacco pouch, he told me that he did not smoke. His dog, as silent as himself, was friendly without being servile.

It was understood from the first that I should spend the night there; the nearest village was still more than a day and a half away. And besides I was perfectly familiar with the nature of the rare villages in that region. There were four or five of them scattered well apart from each other on these mountain slopes, among white oak thickets, at the extreme end of the wagon roads. They were inhabited by charcoalburners, and the living was bad. Families, crowded together in a climate that is excessively harsh both in winter and in summer, found no escape from the unceasing conflict of personalities. Irrational ambition reached inordinate proportions in the continual desire for escape. The men took their wagonloads of charcoal to the town, then returned. The soundest characters broke under the perpetual grind. The women nursed their grievances. There was rivalry in everything, over the price of charcoal as over a pew in the church, over warring virtues as over warring vice as well as over the ceaseless combat between virtue and vice. And over all there was the wind, also ceaseless, to rasp upon the nerves. There were epidemics of suicide and frequent cases of insanity, usually homicidal.

The shepherd went to fetch a small sack and poured out a heap of acorns on the table. He began to inspect them, one by one, with great concentration, separating the good from the bad. I smoked my pipe. I did offer to help him. He told me that it was his job. And in fact, seeing the care he devoted to the task, I did not insist. That was the whole of our conversation. When he had set aside a large enough pile of good acorns he counted them out by tens, meanwhile eliminating the small ones or those which were slightly cracked, for now he examined them more closely. When he had thus selected one hundred perfect acorns he stopped and we went to bed.

There was peace in being with this man. The next day I asked if I might rest here for a day. He found it quite natural — or, to be more exact, he gave me the impression that nothing could startle him. The rest was not absolutely necessary, but I was interested and wished to know more about him. He opened the pen and led his flock to pasture. Before leaving, he plunged his sack of carefully selected and counted acorns into a pail of water.

I noticed that he carried for a stick an iron rod as thick as my thumb and about a yard and a half long. Resting myself by walking, I followed a path parallel to his. His pasture was in a valley. He left the dog in charge of the little flock and climbed toward where I stood. I was afraid that he was about to rebuke me for my indiscretion, but it was not that at all: this was the way he was going, and he invited me to go along if I had nothing better to do. He climbed to the top of the ridge, about a hundred yards away.

There he began thrusting his iron rod into the earth, making a hole in which he planted an acorn; then he refilled the hole. He was planting oak trees. I asked him if the land belonged to him. He answered no. Did he know whose it was? He did not. He supposed it was community property, or perhaps belonged to people who cared nothing about it. He was not interested in finding out whose it was. He planted his hundred acorns with the greatest care.

JEAN GIONO   After the midday meal he resumed his planting. I suppose I must have been fairly insistent in my questioning, for he answered me. For three years he had been planting trees in this wilderness. He had planted one hundred thousand. Of the hundred thousand, twenty thousand had sprouted. Of the twenty thousand he still expected to lose about half, to rodents or to the unpredictable designs of Providence. There remained ten thousand oak trees to grow where nothing had grown before.

That was when I began to wonder about the age of this man. He was obviously over fifty. Fifty-five, he told me. His name was Elzéard Bouffier. He had once had a farm in the lowlands. There he had had his life. He had lost his only son, then his wife. He had withdrawn into this solitude where his pleasure was to live leisurely with his lambs and his dog. It was his opinion that this land was dying for want of trees. He added that, having no very pressing business of his own, he had resolved to remedy this state of affairs.

Since I was at that time, in spite of my youth, leading a solitary life, I understood how to deal gently with solitary spirits. But my very youth forced me to consider the future in relation to myself and to a certain quest for happiness. I told him that in thirty years his ten thousand oaks would be magnificent. He answered quite simply that if God granted him life, in thirty years he would have planted so many more that these ten thousand would be like a drop of water in the ocean.

Besides, he was now studying the reproduction of beech trees and had a nursery of seedlings grown from beechnuts near his cottage. The seedlings, which he had protected from his sheep with a wire fence, were very beautiful. He was also considering birches for the valleys where, he told me, there was a certain amount of moisture a few yards below the surface of the soil.

The next day, we parted.

The following year came the War of 1914, in which I was involved for the next five years. An infantryman hardly had time for reflecting upon trees. To tell the truth, the thing itself had made no impression upon me; I had considered it as a hobby, a stamp collection, and forgotten it.

The war over, I found myself possessed of a tiny demobilization bonus and a huge desire to breathe fresh air for a while. It was with no other objective that I again took the road to the barren lands.

The countryside had not changed. However, beyond the deserted village I glimpsed in the distance a sort of greyish mist that covered the mountaintops like a carpet. Since the day before, I had begun to think again of the shepherd tree-planter. "Ten thousand oaks," I reflected, "really take up quite a bit of space."

I had seen too many men die during those five years not to imagine easily that Elzéard Bouffier was dead, especially since, at twenty, one regards men of fifty as old men with nothing left to do but die. He was not dead. As a matter of fact, he was extremely spry. He had changed jobs. Now he had only four sheep but, instead, a hundred beehives. He had got rid of the sheep because they threatened his young trees. For, he told me (and I saw for myself), the war had disturbed him not at all. He had imperturbably continued to plant.

The oaks of 1910 were then ten years old and taller than either of us. It was an impressive spectacle. I was literally speechless and, as he did not talk, we spent the whole day walking in silence through his forest. In three sections, it measured eleven kilometers in length and three kilometers at its greatest width. When you remembered that all this had sprung from the hands and the soul of this one man, without technical resources, you understood that men could be as effectual as God in other realms than that of destruction.

He had pursued his plan, and beech trees as high as my shoulder, spreading out as far as the eye could reach, confirmed it. He showed me handsome clumps of birch planted five years before — that is, in 1915, when I had been fighting at Verdun. He had set them out in all the valleys where he had guessed — and rightly — that there was moisture almost at the surface of the ground. They were as delicate as young girls, and very well established.

Creation seemed to come about in a sort of chain reaction. He did not worry about it; he was determinedly pursuing his task in all its simplicity; but as we went back toward the village I saw water flowing in brooks that had been dry since the memory of man. This was the most impressive result of chain reaction that I had seen. These dry streams had once, long ago, run with water. Some of the dreary villages I mentioned before had been built on the sites of ancient Roman settlements, traces of which still remained; and archaeologists, exploring there, had found fishhooks where, in the twentieth century, cisterns were needed to assure a small supply of water.

The wind, too, scattered seeds. As the water reappeared, so there reappeared willows, rushes, meadows, gardens, flowers, and a certain purpose in being alive. But the transformation took place so gradually that it became part of the pattern without causing any astonishment. Hunters, climbing into the wilderness in pursuit of hares or wild boar, had of course noticed the sudden growth of little trees, but had attributed it to some natural caprice of the earth. That is why no one meddled with Elzéard Bouffier's work. If he had been detected he would have had opposition. He was undetectable. Who in the villages or in the administration could have dreamed of such perseverance in a magnificent generosity?

To have anything like a precise idea of this exceptional character one must not forget that he worked in total solitude: so total that, toward the end of his life, he lost the habit of speech. Or perhaps it was that he saw no need for it.

In 1933 he received a visit from a forest ranger who notified him of an order against lighting fires out of doors for fear of endangering the growth of this *natural* forest. It was the first time, the man told him naively, that he had ever heard of a forest growing of its own accord. At that time Bouffier was about to plant beeches at a spot some twelve kilometers from his cottage. In order to avoid travelling back and forth — for he was then seventy-five — he planned to build a stone cabin right at the plantation. The next year he did so.

In 1935 a whole delegation came from the Government to examine the "natural forest." There was a high official from the Forest Service, a deputy, technicians. There was a great deal of ineffectual talk. It was decided that something must be done and, fortunately, nothing was done except the only helpful thing: the whole forest was placed under the protection of the State, and charcoal burning prohibited. For it was impossible not to be captivated by the beauty of those young trees in the fullness of health, and they cast their spell over the deputy himself.

A friend of mine was among the forestry officers of the delegation. To him I explained the mystery. One day the following week we went together to see Elzéard Bouffier. We found him hard at work, some ten kilometers from the spot where the inspection had taken place.

This forester was not my friend for nothing. He was aware of values. He knew how to keep silent. I delivered the eggs I had brought as a present. We shared our lunch among the three of us and spent several hours in wordless contemplation of the countryside.

In the direction from which we had come the slopes were covered with trees twenty to twenty-five feet tall. I remembered how the land had looked in 1913: a desert....Peaceful, regular toil, the vigorous mountain air, frugality and, above all, serenity of spirit had endowed this old man with awe-inspiring health. He was one of God's athletes. I wondered how many more acres he was going to cover with trees.

Before leaving, my friend simply made a brief suggestion about certain species of trees that the soil here seemed particularly suited for. He did not force the point. "For the very good reason," he told me later, "that Bouffier knows more about it than I do." At the end of an hour's walking — having turned it over in his mind — he added, "He knows a lot more about it than anybody. He's discovered a wonderful way to be happy!"

It was thanks to this officer that not only the forest but also the happiness of the man was protected. He delegated three rangers to the task, and so terrorized them that they remained proof against all the bottles of wine the charcoalburners could offer.

The only serious danger to the work occurred during the war of 1939. As cars were being run on gazogenes (woodburning generators), there was never enough wood. Cutting was started among the oaks of 1910, but the area was so far from any railroads that the enterprise turned out to be financially unsound. It was abandoned. The shepherd had seen nothing of it. He was thirty kilometers away, peacefully continuing his work, ignoring the war of '39 as he had that of '14.

I saw Elzéard Bouffier for the last time in June of 1945. He was then eighty-seven. I had started back along the route through the wastelands;

JEAN GIONO   but now, in spite of the disorder in which the war had left the country, there was a bus running between the Durance Valley and the mountain. I attributed the fact that I no longer recognized the scenes of my earlier journeys to this relatively speedy transportation. It seemed to me, too, that the route took me through new territory. It took the name of a village to convince me that I was actually in that region that had been all ruins and desolation.

The bus put me down at Vergons. In 1913 this hamlet of ten or twelve houses had three inhabitants.

They had been savage creatures, hating one another, living by trapping game, little removed, both physically and morally from the conditions of prehistoric man. All about them nettles were feeding upon the remains of abandoned houses.

Their condition had been beyond hope. For them, nothing but to await death — a situation which rarely predisposes to virtue.

Everything was changed. Even the air. Instead of the harsh dry winds that used to attack me, a gentle breeze was blowing, laden with scents. A sound like water came from the mountains: it was the wind in the forest. Most amazing of all, I heard the actual sound of water falling into a pool. I saw that a fountain had been built, that it flowed freely and — what touched me most — that someone had planted a linden beside it, a linden that must have been four years old, already in full leaf, the incontestable symbol of resurrection.

Besides, Vergons bore evidence of labour at the sort of undertaking for which hope is required. Hope, then, had returned. Ruins had been cleared away, dilapidated walls torn down and five houses restored. Now there were twenty-eight inhabitants, four of them young married couples. The new houses, freshly plastered, were surrounded by gardens where vegetables and flowers grew in orderly confusion, cabbages and roses, leeks and snapdragons, celery and anemones. It was now a village where one would like to live.

From that point on I went on foot. The war just finished had not yet allowed the full blooming of life, but Lazarus was out of the tomb. On the lower slopes of the mountain I saw little fields of barley and of rye; deep in the narrow valleys the meadows were turning green.

It has taken only the eight years since then for the whole countryside to glow with health and prosperity. On the site of ruins I had seen in 1913 now stand neat farms, cleanly plastered, testifying to a happy and comfortable life. The old streams, fed by the rains and snows that the forest conserves, are flowing again. Their waters have been channelled. On each farm, in groves of maples, fountain pools over flow onto carpets of fresh mint. Little by little the villages have been rebuilt. People from the plains, where land is costly, have settled here, bringing youth, motion, the spirit of adventure. Along the road you meet hearty men and women, boys and girls who understand laughter and have recovered a taste for picnics. Counting the former population, unrecognizable now that they live in comfort, more than ten thousand people owe their happiness to Elzéard Bouffier.

When I reflect that one man, armed only with his own physical and moral resources, was able to cause this land of Canaan to spring from the wasteland, I am convinced that in spite of everything, humanity is admirable. But when I compute the unfailing greatness of spirit and the tenacity of benevolence that it must have taken to achieve this result, I am taken with an immense respect for that old and unlearned peasant who was able to complete a work worthy of God.

Elzéard Bouffier died peacefully in 1947 at the hospice in Banon.

THE THRILL

of

THE GRASS

W.P. KINSELLA

1981: the summer the baseball players went on strike. The dull weeks drag by, the summer deepens, the strike is nearly a month old. Outside the city the corn rustles and ripens in the sun. Summer without baseball: a disruption to the psyche. An unexplainable aimlessness engulfs me. I stay later and later each evening in the small office at the rear of my shop. Now, driving home after work, the worst of the rush hour traffic over, it is the time of evening I would normally be heading for the stadium.

I enjoy arriving an hour early, parking in a far corner of the lot, walking slowly toward the stadium, rays of sun dropping softly over my shoulders like tangerine ropes, my shadow gliding with me, black as an umbrella. I like to watch young families beside their campers, the mothers in shorts, grilling hamburgers, their men drinking beer. I enjoy seeing little boys dressed in the home team uniform, barely toddling, clutching hotdogs in upraised hands.

I am a failed shortstop. As a young man, I saw myself diving to my left, graceful as a toppling tree, fielding high grounders like a cat leaping for butterflies, bracing my right foot and tossing to first, the throw true as if a steel ribbon connected my hand and the first baseman's glove. I dreamed of leading the American League in hitting — being inducted into the Hall of Fame. I batted .217 in my senior year of high school and averaged 1.3 errors per nine innings.

I know the stadium will be deserted; nevertheless I wheel my car down off the freeway, park, and walk across the silent lot, my footsteps rasping and mournful. Strangle-grass and creeping charlie are already inching up through the gravel, surreptitious, surprised at their own ease. Faded bottle caps, rusted bits of chrome, an occasional paper clip, recede in the earth. I circle a ticket booth, sun-faded, empty, the door closed by an oversized padlock. I walk beside the tall, machinery-green, board fence. A half mile away a few cars hiss along the freeway; overhead a single-engine plane fizzes lazily. The whole place is silent as an empty classroom, like a house suddenly without children. It is then that I spot the door-shape. I have to check twice to be sure it is there: a door cut in the deep green boards of the fence, more the promise of a door than the real thing, the kind of door, as children, we cut in the sides of cardboard boxes with our mother's paring knives. As I move closer, a golden circle of lock, like an acrimonious eye, establishes its certainty.

I stand, my nose so close to the door I can smell the faint odour of paint, the golden eye of a lock inches from my own eyes. My desire to be inside the ballpark is so great that for the first time in my life I commit a criminal act. I have been a locksmith for over forty years. I take the small tools from the pocket of my jacket, and in less time than it would take a speedy runner to circle the bases I am inside the stadium. Though the ballpark is open-air, it smells of abandonment; the walkways and seating areas are cold as basements. I breathe the odours of rancid popcorn and wilted cardboard.

The maintenance staff were laid off when the strike began. Synthetic grass does not need to be cut or watered. I stare down at the ball diamond, where just to the right of the pitcher's mound, a single weed, perhaps two inches high, stands defiant in the rain-pocked dirt.

The field sits breathless in the orangy glow of the evening sun. I stare at the potato-coloured earth of the infield, that wide, dun arc, surrounded by plastic grass. As I contemplate the prickly turf, which scorches the thighs and buttocks of a sliding player as if he were being seared by hot steel, it stares back in its uniform ugliness. The seams that send routinely hit ground balls veering at tortuous angles, are vivid, grey as scars.

I remember the ballfields of my childhood, the outfields full of soft hummocks and brown-eyed gopher holes.

I stride down from the stands and and walk out to the middle of the field. I touch the stubble that is called grass, take off my shoes, but find it is like walking on a row of toothbrushes. It was an evil

W.P. HINSELLA day when they stripped the sod from this ballpark, cut it into yard-wide swathes, rolled it, memories and all, into great green-and-black cinnamonroll shapes, trucked it away. Nature temporarily defeated. But Nature is patient.

Over the next few days an idea forms within me, ripening, selling, pushing everything else into a corner. It is like knowing a new, wonderful joke and not being able to share. I need an accomplice.

I go to see a man I don't know personally, though I have seen his face peering at me from the financial pages of the local newspaper, and the *Wall Street Journal*, and I have been watching his profile at the baseball stadium, two boxes to the right of me, for several years. He is a fan. Really a fan. When the weather is intemperate, or the game not close, the people around us disappear like flowers closing at sunset, but we are always there until the last pitch. I know he is a man who attends because of the beauty and mystery of the game, a man who can sit during the last of the ninth with the game decided innings ago, and draw joy from watching the first baseman adjust the angle of his glove as the pitcher goes into his windup.

He, like me, is a first-base-side fan. I've always watched baseball from behind first base. The positions fans choose at sporting events are like politics, religion, or philosophy: a view of the world, a way of seeing the universe. They make no sense to anyone, have no basis in anything but stubbornness.

I brought up my daughters to watch baseball from the first-base side. One lives in Japan and sends me box scores from the Japanese newspapers, and Japanese baseball magazines with pictures of superstars politely bowing to one another. She has a season ticket in Yokohama; on the first-base side.

"Tell him a baseball fan is here to see him," is all I will say to his secretary. His office is in a skyscraper, from which he can look out over the city to where the prairie rolls green as mountain water to the limits of the eye. I wait all afternoon in the artificially cool, glassy reception area with its yellow and mauve chairs, chrome and glass coffee tables. Finally, in the late afternoon, my message is passed along.

"I've seen you at the baseball stadium," I say, not introducing myself.

"Yes," he says. "I recognize you. Three rows back, about eight seats to my left. You have a red scorebook and you often bring your daughter...."

"Granddaughter. Yes, she goes to sleep in my lap in the late innings, but she knows how to calculate an ERA and she's only in Grade 2."

"One of my greatest regrets," says this tall man, whose moustache and carefully styled hair are polar-bear white, "is that my grandchildren all live over a thousand miles away. You're very lucky. Now, what can I do for you?"

"I have an idea," I say. "One that's been creeping towards me like a first baseman when the bunt sign is on. What do you think about artificial turf?"

"Hmmmf," he snorts, "that's what the strike should be about. Baseball is meant to be played on summer evenings and Sunday afternoons, on grass just cut by a horse-drawn mower," and we smile as our eyes meet.

"I've just discovered the ballpark is open, to me anyway," I go on. "There's no one there while the strike is on. The wind blows through the high top of the grandstand, whining until the pigeons in the rafters flutter. It's lonely as a ghost town."

"And what is it you do there, alone with the pigeons?"

"I dream."

"And where do I come in?"

"You've always struck me as a man who dreams. I think we have things in common. I think you might like to come with me. I could show you what I dream, paint you pictures, suggest what might happen..."

He studies me carefully for a moment, like a pitcher trying to decide if he can trust the sign his catcher has just given him.

"Tonight?" he says. "Would tonight be too soon?"

"Park in the northwest corner of the lot about 1:00 am. There is a door about fifty yards to the right of the main gate. I'll open it when I hear you."

He nods.

I turn and leave.

The night is clear and cotton warm when he arrives. "Oh, my," he

THE THRILL OF THE GRASS

W.P. HINSELLA   says, staring at the stadium turned chrome-blue by a full moon. "Oh, my," he says again, breathing in the faint odours of baseball, the reminder of fans and players not long gone.

"Let's go down to the field," I say. I am carrying a cardboard pizza box, holding it on the upturned palms of my hands, like an offering.

When we reach the field, he first stands on the mound, makes an awkward attempt at a windup, then does a little sprint from first to about halfway to second. "I think I know what you've brought," he says, gesturing toward the box, "but let me see anyway."

I open the box in which rests a square foot of sod, the grass smooth and pure, cool as a swatch of satin, fragile as baby's hair.

"Ohhh," the man says, reaching out a finger to test the moistness of it. "Oh, I see."

We walk across the field, the harsh, prickly turf making the bottoms of my feet tingle, to the leftfield corner where, in the angle formed by the foul line and the warning track, I lay down the square foot of sod. "That's beautiful," my friend says, kneeling beside me, placing his hand, fingers spread wide, on the verdant square, leaving a print faint as a veronica.

I take from my belt a sickle-shaped blade, the kind used for cutting carpet. I measure along the edge of the sod, dig the point in and pull carefully toward me. There is a ripping sound, like tearing an old bed sheet. I hold up the square of artificial turf like something freshly killed, while all the time digging the sharp point into the packed earth I have exposed. I replace the sod lovingly, covering the newly bared surface.

"A protest," I say.

"But it could be more," the man replies.

"I hoped you'd say that. It could be. If you'd like to come back..."

"Tomorrow night?"

"Tomorrow night would be fine. But there will be an admission charge..."

"A square of sod?"

"A square of sod two inches thick..."

"Of the same grass?"

"Of the same grass. But there's more."

"I suspected as much."

"You must have a friend..."

"Who would join us?"

"Yes."

"I have two. Would that be all right?"

"I trust your judgement."

"My father. He's over eighty," my friend says. "You might have seen him with me once or twice. He lives over fifty miles from here, but if I call him he'll come. And my friend..."

"If they pay their admission they'll be welcome..."

"And they may have friends..."

"Indeed they may. But what will we do with this?" I say, holding up the sticky-backed square of turf, which smells of glue and fabric.

"We could mail them anonymously to baseball executives, politicians, clergymen."

"Gentle reminders not to tamper with Nature."

We dance toward the exit, rampant with excitement.

"You will come back? You'll bring the others?"

"Count on it," says my friend.

They do come, those trusted friends, and friends of friends, each making a live, green deposit. At first, a tiny row of sod squares begins to inch along toward left-centre field. The next night even more people arrive, the following night more again, and the night after there is positively a crowd. Those who come once seem always to return accompanied by friends, occasionally a son or younger brother, but mostly men my age or older, for we are the ones who remember the grass.

Night after night the pilgrimage continues. The first night I stand inside the deep green door, listening. I hear a vehicle stop; hear a car door close with a snug thud. I open the door when the sound of soft soled shoes on gravel tells me it is time. The door swings silent as a snake. We nod curt greetings to each other. Two men pass me, each carrying a grasshopper-legged sprinkler. Later, each sprinkler will sizzle like frying onions as it wheels, a silver sparkler in the moonlight.

During the nights that follow, I stand sentinel-like at the top of the grandstand, watching as my cohorts arrive. Old men walking

W. P. KINSELLA   across a parking lot in a row, in the dark, carrying coiled hoses, looking like the many wheels of a locomotive, old men who have slipped away from their homes, skulked down their sturdy sidewalks, breathing the cool, grassy, after-midnight air. They have left behind their sleeping, grey-haired women, their immaculate bungalows, their manicured lawns. They continue to walk across the parking lot, while occasionally a soft wheeze, a nibbling, breathy sound like an old horse might make, divulges their humanity. They move methodically toward the baseball stadium which hulks against the moon-blue sky like a small mountain. Beneath the tint of starlight, the tall light standards which rise above the fences and grandstand glow purple, necks bent forward, like sunflowers heavy with seed.

My other daughter lives in this city, is married to a fan, but one who watches baseball from behind the third base. And like marrying outside the faith, she has been converted to the third-base side. They have their own season tickets, twelve rows up just to the outfield side of third base. I love her, but I don't trust her enough to let her in on my secret.

I could trust my granddaughter, but she is too young. At her age she shouldn't have to face such responsibility. I remember my own daughter, the one who lives in Japan, remember her at nine, all knees, elbows and missing teeth — remember peering in her room, seeing her asleep, a shower of well-thumbed baseball cards scattered over her chest and pillow.

I haven't been able to tell my wife — it is like my compatriots and I are involved in a ritual for true believers only. Maggie, who knew me when I still dreamed of playing professionally myself — Maggie, after over half a lifetime together, comes and sits in my lap in the comfortable easy chair which has adjusted through the years to my thickening shape, just as she has. I love to hold the lightness of her, her tongue exploring my mouth, gently as a baby's finger.

"Where do you go?" she asks sleepily when I crawl into bed at dawn.

I mumble a reply. I know she doesn't sleep well when I'm gone. I can feel her body rhythms change as I slip out of bed after midnight.

"Aren't you too old to be having a change of life," she says, placing her toast-warm hand on my cold thigh.

I am not the only one with this problem.

"I'm developing a reputation," whispers an affable man at the ballpark. "I imagine any number of private investigators following any number of cars across the city. I imagine them creeping about the parking lot, shining pen-lights on licence plates, trying to guess what we're up to. Think of the reports they must prepare. I wonder if our wives are disappointed that we're not out discoing with frizzy-haired teenagers?"

Night after night, virtually no words are spoken. Each man seems to know his assignment. Not all bring sod. Some carry rakes, some hoes, some hoses, which, when joined together, snake across the infield and outfield, dispensing the blessing of water. Others cradle in their arms bags of earth for building up the infield to meet the thick, living sod.

I often remain high in the stadium, looking down on the men moving over the earth, dark as ants, each sodding, cutting, watering, shaping. Occasionally the moon finds a knife blade as it trims the sod or slices away a chunk of artificial turf, and tosses the reflection skyward like a bright ball. My body tingles. There should be symphony music playing. Everyone should be humming "America the Beautiful."

Towards dawn, I watch the men walking away in groups, like small patrols of soldiers, carrying instead of arms, the tools and utensils which breathe life back into the arid ballfield.

Row by row, night by night, we lay the little squares of sod, moist as chocolate cake with green icing. Where did all the sod come from? I picture many men, in many parts of the city, surreptitiously cutting chunks out of their own lawns in the leafy midnight darkness, listening to the uncomprehending protests of their wives the next day — pretending to know nothing of it — pretending to have called the police to investigate.

When the strike is over I know we will all be here to watch the workouts, to hear the recalcitrant joints crackling like twigs after the forced inactivity. We will sit in our regular seats, scattered like popcorn throughout the stadium, and we'll nod as we pass on the way to the exits, exchange secret smiles, proud as new fathers.

For me, the best part of all will be the surprise. I feel like a

W. P. Hinsella magician who has gestured hypnotically and produced an elephant from thin air. I know I am not alone in my wonder. I know that rockets shoot off in half-a-hundred chests, the excitement of birthday mornings, Christmas eves, and home-town doubleheaders, boils within each of my conspirators. Our secret rites have been performed with love, like delivering a valentine to a sweetheart's door in that blue-steel span of morning just before dawn.

Players and management are meeting round the clock. A settlement is imminent. I have watched the stadium covered square foot by square foot until it looks like green graph paper. I have stood and felt the cool odours of the grass rise up and touch my face. I have studied the lines between each small square, watched those lines fade until they were visible to my eyes alone, then not even to them.

What will the players think, as they straggle into the stadium and find the miracle we have created? The old-timers will raise their heads like ponies, as far away as the parking lot, when the thrill of the grass reaches their nostrils. And, as they dress, they'll recall sprawling in the lush outfields of childhood, the grass as cool as a mother's hand on a forehead.

"Goodbye, goodbye," we say at the gate, the smell of water, of sod, of sweat, small perfumes in the air. Our secrets are safe with each other. We go our separate ways.

Alone in the stadium in the last chill darkness before dawn, I drop to my hands and knees in the centre of the outfield. My palms are sodden. Water touches the skin between my spread fingers. I lower my face to the silvered grass, which, wonder of wonders, already has the ephemeral odours of baseball about it.

Little Paradise

ZENA COLLIER

There was no longer any doubt about it; they were lost. This was their first time on the creek from which this maze of narrow waterways derived, winding around in convoluted curves, dotted at frequent intervals with tiny uninhabited islands, all of which looked alike. A friend had recommended the area. "Great for canoeing. Pleasing prospects at every turn. None of those damn speedboats and water-skiers." For the past hour, in fact, they had seen no other boats at all: no canoes or dinghies, no cabin cruisers with their seemingly mandatory quota of bluff types wearing commodore hats, holding martini glasses or beer. (Earlier that day, one such, at sight of their canoe, had leaned over the rail, hollering at them, flapping a hand back and forth against his mouth to produce what was meant to be a war whoop. "Hey, you Tarzan, she Jane, huh?" Laughter.)

"What time is it getting to be?" Peter asked.

"Just gone five." Frances rested her paddle for a moment.

They had been out since ten. All day the sun had shone from a cloudless sky, dappling the leaves of the branches that dipped over the water, stippling the water with shade. Insects with gossamer wings hummed past. Occasionally the *ts, ts, ts* of a cedar waxwing, the dry rattle of a kingfisher, broke the silence. Otherwise all was still.

It was the kind of day on which they congratulated themselves on their acquisition of the canoe. For people of their taste and principles, the canoe had proved an ideal choice. It offered no disturbance, by noise or pollution, to its passengers or to nature; it required no particular skill, maintenance, or expensive berthing. Best of all, it

ZENA COLLIER   made easily possible days of escape from the tensions of their everyday lives. Peter, a thin dark man with a face all angles, was a graphics designer who had recently left his agency job to freelance. Frances, redhaired, with a pleasant down-to-earth manner, was a socialworker attached to one of the great metropolitan hospitals. For both of them, a Saturday spent this way brought a necessary renewal of the spirit.

It was with regret that they'd decided at four o'clock to start for home. They were due at a party at seven; it was going to take them a while to paddle back to the point of starting, then the drive home would take the better part of an hour. So they had turned around and headed back, stroking steadily. Until they'd become aware, suddenly, that they had passed the same spot twice; they recognized it because of an uprooted tree which lay in the water, its exposed roots forming a natural driftwood sculpture upon which someone had tossed, or placed, a beer can. ("Look at that," Frances had said earlier, shaking her head. The trappings of their midday meal — paper plates, napkins, the bottle emptied of wine — had been carefully stowed in a paper bag and replaced in the canoe, to be properly disposed of on their arrival home.)

"We must have gone in a circle," Frances said.

"Keep going left. We'll hit the creek further on."

They resumed paddling.

"Are you tired?" Peter asked, after a while.

"No." In fact, she had begun to ache between the shoulder blades, but she knew that if she said so, Peter would suggest putting on the motor and she didn't want that.

When he had first bought the motor, she had been very much against it. An outboard on a canoe was surely a contradiction? But there was a point to it, Peter maintained. "We'll use it just to reach the outskirts of more remote areas, then take it off." Still, the sound of the engine starting up always jarred her unpleasantly, and ruined, she felt, the peace; she disapproved, too, of the trail of blue smoke it occasionally emitted, though Peter said that was just a matter of some needed adjustment.

"That island over there, with the willows, did we pass it before?"

"I don't know. They all look alike. Can't you tell from the sun?"

"I *thought* I could." He sounded exasperated.

"We're never going to make the Robsons' by seven."

Minutes later, the sound of the engine cut the still air, and they were moving along at a steady rate. But with little success. "We passed this before. I remember those sumacs…"

"Yes," Peter said wearily. "Now what?"

"Let's try over there." Frances pointed. "There was an inlet. Perhaps it leads somewhere."

The inlet narrowed after the first few metres, the banks growing gradually higher and closer. Soon the trees met overhead in a solid archway, the foliage forming a verdant tunnel as the passage between grew narrower and narrower.

Frances shivered. How dark it seemed, and cold…. Had the sun gone permanently, or was it just —

"We're coming out!"

Abruptly they were out of the dimness, out of the tunnel, finding themselves on a sunlit lake, a pond, really, perhaps a hundred metres across, with shallow sloping banks covered with woodland.

"Look!"

Across the pond was a house set almost at the water's edge, and beside it a redwood table where people sat, adults and children.

"Thank heaven! We can ask directions."

The people watched as the canoe put-putted across the pond toward them. In the still and sunlit scene, the motor sounded terribly loud. A desecration, Frances thought, regretting it, sorry not only to be invading these people's privacy but to be disturbing the peace of this serene spot.

But the adults — two women and two men — smiled at them as the canoe approached. Peter idled the motor then reached out and kept his hand on the bank, steadying the canoe as he talked.

"Sorry to disturb you, but we're lost. How do we get back to the start of Forked Creek?"

One of the men stood up and approached. "You're a long way off. It'll take you quite a while."

"Not with this," Peter nodded at the motor. But just then, as though on cue, the motor died. "Damn! Out of gas, I'm afraid. Can you by any chance let me have some fuel?"

"Sorry, we haven't any. We've no cars or powerboats or any such thing."

The others came over. The men admired the canoe and asked questions about the motor; they said they hadn't seen a motor on a canoe before. The children — a boy and girl in their early teens, and a little girl who seemed about five — stood watching and listening. The little girl said shyly, "I'm glad you're going to stay."

One of the women rumpled the child's blond curly hair.

"This is my daughter Cassandra — Cassie."

Frances smiled at Cassie, an engaging child with sturdy, golden-brown baby-fat limbs. The whole group, in fact, was glowing with health, tanned by sun and wind; the women's dimpling smiles showed white even teeth; the men were tall, broad shouldered, muscular, friendly.

"Would you care to join us for something to eat?" the other woman asked. "We're just starting dinner."

"Please do," Cassie's mother urged. "Just family style. I'm Amy Carner, by the way, and this is my husband Robert, and his brother Martin and Martin's wife Lorraine. And their twins, Andy and Jennifer."

"Do stay," Lorraine said. "Food'll give you energy for the return trip home. We'd love to have you."

"Yes, we would," Martin said.

Peter glanced at Frances. "We wouldn't want to impose —"

"No imposition at all," Robert said. "We don't get many visitors. Just, occasionally, people like yourselves, who end up here lost."

"Thtay, thtay," Cassie pleaded, her finger in her mouth.

Frances's eyes met Peter's. The smell of meat cooking on the outdoor fireplace wafted over enticingly. They had eaten nothing at all for hours. And the Robsons were a lost cause by now.

"That's awfully kind of you. If you're sure —"

For answer, Robert bent down and pulled the canoe in to the bank. Martin put out a hand and helped Frances alight. Lorraine took them into the house to wash up.

Outside again, at the table, Frances realized just how hungry she was. She and Peter ate with enormous appetite. All the food was delicious: the salads and corn were homegrown; the steaks and hots were the best she'd ever tasted, Frances thought and said so.

"This is a beautiful spot ..." She glanced at the pond lying still as glass beneath the sun, at the greenness of the trees reflected in the water. No sign, besides themselves, of human habitation; nothing to spoil or disturb the scene's tranquillity. "It must be lovely here in winter, too. Do you live here all year round?" she asked.

Amy nodded. It was like a Christmas card scene in winter, she said, when the pond froze and snow lay on the woods and the hills beyond.

"Though lately some rackety snowmobiles have come through." Martin sliced more meat and proffered the platter. "A couple of 'em came to a sticky end near here. Ever ridden one?"

"Not I." Peter took a bite of steak.

"Hate them," Frances said. "Fouling up the countryside."

Robert gave her a glance. "Yet you put on a motor—"

"That," Peter said, "was my idea. Fran was against it. But we only use it for certain contingencies."

"We've a rowboat, ourselves." Martin speared another sausage.

Lorraine passed potato salad.

"We do what we can, in our way, to preserve —"

"In our small way," Amy said. "Meat? Tomatoes, Peter? Frances?"

Not another thing, they protested, smiling, not another morsel of steak or succulent sausage, sun-warm tomato or butterclad corn.

For dessert there was cherry pie with iced tea.

"Delicious." Peter slowly sipped the cool amber liquid. "Different."

Yes, it was an herbal tea, Amy said, her own recipe.

Frances drank hers slowly, leaving half — she'd never liked any kind of tea.

The sun lay low on the horizon now. Frances and Peter helped carry things into the house.

Andy and Jennifer appeared with fishing rods. "Where's the boat?"

"Being caulked," Robert said. "You can't take it."

"Oh." Andy turned to Peter. "Would it be okay if we use your canoe?

They bite better out in the middle of the pond."

Peter hesitated. "We have to be getting along pretty soon."

Very soon, Frances thought; the canoe had no light, and being out on the water at night was not an inviting prospect.

"Is twenty minutes any good to you?"

"Great," Andy said. "Thanks a lot."

Cassie slipped her hand into Frances's. "Come and play with me."

"What shall we play?"

"I'll show you."

Cassie led her outdoors, round to the other side of the house. On a small patch of flagstone, she demonstrated a game played with coins, using the coins as play objects — a kind of Pitch Pebble. She had a large stock of coins, of all denominations, kept in what was obviously an old purse of her mother's.

Once, as they played, a quarter pitched clumsily by Frances ended up in the grass. They searched but to no avail. "I'm sorry, Cassie."

"It doesn't matter. It's only game money."

"But —"

"I'll get more." Cassie said. "There's more when I want it. Daddy gives it to me."

They played several games. By now the house glimmered palely through the dusk; the shadows of evening were thickening everywhere.

Frances straightened. "That's it, Cassie. I have to go home now."

Cassie did not argue, just stood silent, finger in her mouth, as Frances turned and went in search of Peter,

She found him on the bank, with the others, looking out over the water. "Peter, shouldn't we —"

"Yes, we have to be getting along." He turned to the others. "We're very grateful for all your hospitality."

"You've been so kind." Frances said. "That marvellous dinner... this idyllic setting. Thank you for letting us share your little paradise."

"Must you rush off?"

"How about a drink? One for the road, as it were?"

They really had to get going, Peter said. "But thank you again, for everything."

Martin cupped his hands around his mouth. "Andy! Jennifer!" His voice rang across the dark mass of water. "Come along! Our guests are leaving!"

By now the youngsters were almost completely invisible. Andy's voice, floating back, seemed disembodied, "Just a minute — something's biting!"

Frances glanced at Peter, who shrugged. Clearly they would have to wait; they could hardly spoil the children's fun after accepting their parents' gracious hospitality.

"You see, you'll just have to come in for a nightcap."

Martin's hand descended on Peter's shoulder.

They sat around the living room, sipping a liquer that Robert poured. Not the sort of thing Frances liked usually — and Peter, she knew, didn't care for it at all — an elderberry wine, or something like that, that Robert had made.

It must be the wine, combined with the rigours of the day, that was making her feel so sleepy now, she thought; it took a huge effort to keep her eyelids open. Seconds, later, in fact, she saw with dismay that Peter, slumped on the sofa flanked by Robert and Martin, had yielded; his eyes were closed, his head tilted forward.

Dreadful! She began to stammer some kind of apology for their drowsiness. But where, oh where, were Andy and Jennifer? How could they go on fishing in the darkness like that, especially when they knew the canoe was needed?

As though the thought had given birth to the event, they appeared, carrying fishing gear. She tried to stand, to speak, but her legs were suddenly weak, her vision blurred, her thoughts addled.

Now her head sank irresistibly forward. But though her eyes closed she was not quite asleep, for she heard voices. Or was she in fact asleep and dreaming; were the voices part of the dream?

Not the woman. It wasn't her idea. That was Lorraine.

She's in it just as deeply as him.

Only a canoe...

But the motor... That was Robert.

On and on it went, a kind of debate. Parts of it she missed, as consciousness seemed to ebb and flow, the line lost between dream and reality.

Look. That was Andy. *We found these.*

Silence.

You see? Lorraine again. *They could have tossed that bottle, that trash, overboard. I vote we let them go. Anyway —* Someone walked across the room, drowning out the voice — *hardly worth it... not particularly large...*

Large... The canoe? "Let them go?"

Fear began at the edge of awareness, working inward like a worm in an apple.

Hush, she's stirring!

Someone approached, touched her, spoke her name. She let her head slump further forward.

Not she. They're out, both of them.

I want the money. That was Cassie, whining. *She lost one of my quarters.*

Goodness, child, you ought to be in bed! Amy, take her upstairs its long past her bedtime.

Be a good girl, Cassie, someone else said. *You'll get the money. You always do, don't you?*

Thieves then? Common robbers, lying in wait for unwary boaters? But—

Complimented me on the way I cooked the steaks...

Laughter.

That was funny? The steaks?

A memory: the sight of the meat invitingly singed by the fire. The sausages. "We make them, ourselves," Amy had said.

Her thoughts spun like a Catherine wheel. Her heart pounded harder and harder — surely it would burst the flesh that housed it. Flesh.

Oh God, she must be sick to be thinking this way, as sick as the rest of them, every one of them, the whole picturebook family with the bloom of health, the radiance of summer, upon them. Summer ... And what of winter, the hapless snowmobile riders? Thought stopped at the unthinkable, ran screaming in the other direction. A dream, yes, a nightmare. Any moment now she would awake to see sunlight coming in the bedroom window, would get up, start breakfast, make plans with Peter for their day on the water.

All right. We've talked long enough. Robert cleared his throat.

No denying that sound — the reality of it. The reality of their situation, hers and Peter's here and now. Oh God, Peter, wake up! Though what could they do, even then, the two of them, trapped here? A diversion? What could take their attention, if only for a moment? But they would need, she and Peter, more than a moment to reach the canoe, then get away, paddling, across the water. Unless they left the canoe and tried through the woods. But —

A door slammed. A voice said excitedly, "Dad! Andy! Everybody, come out here!" The girl, Jennifer.

There was a rush of movement, footsteps, the door slammed again, then silence.

A hiss: "Fran!"

She opened her eyes, to meet Peter's. The room was empty except for themselves.

"Did you hear —?"

"Yes! What shall we do?"

"They're coming back! Play dead!"

The door opened again. There were hurrying footsteps, whispers. Robert's voice said, "Shake them, get them up! Hurry!"

A hand on her shoulder shook her, hard.

"Wake up, Frances! Peter! Time to go home. It's getting late." The tone was friendly, just the least bit urgent. "Sleepy? You'll be all right once you're outside."

What was this? For now, dazed, they were being led outside, urged along, hastened down to the canoe in the moonless night. Thick darkness... "You'll want to hurry... It's getting late. The long day must have been too much for you... sleeping like babies...."

Was that all it really was, after all? They had fallen asleep after the meal; it had all been a product of too much food and drink and fatigue?

They were in the canoe now, in the water, helped in by Martin and Lorraine. The canoe rocked. Robert steadied it carefully, placed paddles in their trembling hands. "Owe you an apology ... motor's gone, I'm afraid. Andy and Jenny were fooling around... sank like a stone."

"Never mind!" Peter's voice was almost a croak. "Doesn't matter!" They were off, paddling like demons, shivering, shivering in the sharp night air.

"To the left..." Martin's voice floated after them. "After you're through Scylla and Charybdis, go right three times, then left at the uprooted tree. You'll see it."

They would, for now a moon emerged from the clouds, painting the scene with a frozen light.

"*What happened?*" Frances whispered.

"God knows! Keep going!"

The canoe cut swiftly across the water. But as the darkness of the tunnel yawned before them, Frances hesitated, turned, and saw a cabin cruiser pulling close to shore, several figures on deck. A voice floated across the water. "...don't know how we could have missed our way like that..."

"We must warn them, Peter! We have to warn them!"

He pushed her around. "Keep going. There's nothing we can do."

In the blackness of the tunnel, the only sound was the soft slap of the paddles dipping in the water, while from somewhere far away came the high, screeching giggle of a loon.

My Collection

Dinyar Godrej

I remember my mother washing mulberries before they went off,
first thing in the morning, to send to the neighbours. Or washing
our clothes in a bucket, whites, then coloureds, then socks
until the soap turned to slime. I remember her
dressing up food from previous meals and saving scraps
for passing strays who might linger to guard our house by night.
Upon our travels we carried little bags of tea, sugar, rice,
to save on bills and returned with whatever was going cheap.
She had me convinced my brother's trousers were fashionable
a year after he'd outgrown them. In summer she'd unravel jerseys
and begin to reknit. My father encouraged such thrift
as people who earn in cash do and mother knew there
was no recovering what was laid to waste.
So she gathered, pickled, stewed, cut lights
from old boxes, strewed her flower beds with
fish scales and egg shells and sacrificed
her siesta to shoo parrots from our mango tree.
Once she even made her own shampoo but that
didn't quite work.
          I remember her saving insect-ridden flour, spreading
it out in the noonday blaze, until all that crawled
had crawled away. Old sheets turned
into shoe cloths and dusters, and "good, strong
plastic bags" were saviours of her ripening fruit.
As children we didn't think the secret of her prodigious hands
was in a thousand things she'd transformed or stored away.
We took what she had to give and she didn't stint.

I speak with her monthly on the telephone now —
Am I wearing a vest, do I eat sensibly, then
she puts it down, thinking of the money I spend.

You needn't worry, mother.
Everything is saved. Nothing
is thrown away.

The SYSTEM and the ECOSYSTEM

David Suzuki

The fateful year of 1984 has already long passed and we're only about a decade away from the twenty-first century. What will the world be like then? I do not believe in futurism, the claim that the future can be predicted scientifically. We can extrapolate by projecting trends into coming years, and it is possible to render events more likely by creating self-fulfilling prophesies. But that isn't prediction.

If the future is unknowable, the best strategy for our young people is flexibility and a broadly based education. Most of all, they should have an intimate connection with nature.

Any child who knows that a dragonfly can fly off before it can be grabbed, observes that a seed will germinate and send roots *down* and leaves *up*, watches a squirrel leap deftly from branch to branch, has envied birds soaring effortlessly and has followed a caterpillar through metamorphosis into a butterfly understands that no human technology can ever come close to matching living creatures. Our current technological achievements are impressive by human standards, but measured against the scale of life's complexity, they must be seen as crude and superficial. This perspective has to generate some humility.

A child with love of nature also recognizes that we *share* this planet and that we derive our sustenance from other life forms. If we forget that packaged eggs or hamburger came from animals, a cotton shirt from a plant, a wooden chair from a tree, then we have lost that connection with nature. In November 1985, I watched a performance that brought that reality back into focus.

I was at a meeting in London on the subject of toxic wastes. After my rather ponderous talk, Jack Vallentyne, an ecologist from

DAVID SUZUKI the Centre for Inland Waters in Burlington, got up. Jack wanders the planet carrying a large globe of the Earth resting atop a backpack. It looks... well... unusual. He performs for children around the world by assuming the character of "Johnny Biosphere." Like Johnny Appleseed, Vallentyne plants the seeds of ideas in the fertile soil of children's minds. He put on quite a show, transforming an audience of some 700 self-conscious and sceptical adults into wide-eyed children who shouted answers back to his questions.

The most effective part of Jack's show was the way he demonstrated how much we are a part of the ecosystem. He asked all of us to hold our breath for a few seconds and then informed us we had held gas molecules in our lungs that had been in the lungs of everyone else in the room. Initially, it made us want to stop breathing, but it brought home with a jolt the reality that we share the air with everyone else. Then Jack told us that we all have molecules in our bodies that had once been a part of every single human being who had ever lived in the past 3 000 years! (And he didn't even mention animals and plants.) From Jesus Christ to Marie Curie to Michael Jackson, we are all linked by shared molecules in the air, water, and soil.

Jack then went on to tell us a story about an Indian canoeing on Lake Superior 500 years ago. It was a hot summer day and he was sweating, so he decided to go for a swim. And as that Indian swam in the lake, the sweat washed from his body and was diluted in the lake. Sodium and chloride ions in the sweat diffused through the lake and today, 500 years later, when we take a drink of water in Toronto, we drink sodium and chloride from that Indian's body long ago.

This is a modern description of a spiritual vision of our relationship with all life on earth. It is fitting that his target is children. The difference between Vallentyne's approach and mine is worth noting. I tend to emphasize the destructiveness of a value system that sees humans outside the ecosystem and all of nature as a potential resource. I believe we must recognize that the limited vision of science and technology does not give us control, so then we may try to change directions. My operating faith is in the power of reason to overcome cultural values that are generations old. But it's a bleak picture. Vallentyne uses a radically different approach — his message is just as dark, but it's delivered to children who have not yet accepted all our cultural values. He can revel in the unity of life in the biosphere in a spiritual way that is both uplifting and wonderful. And I think he's on to something.

CHILDREN
ΓIN THE WOODS

BARRY LOPEZ

When I was a child growing up in the San Fernando Valley in California, a trip into Los Angeles was special. The sensation of movement from a rural area into an urban one was sharp. On one of these charged occasions, walking down a sidewalk with my mother, I stopped suddenly, caught by a pattern of sunlight trapped in a spiralling imperfection in a windowpane. A stranger, an elderly woman in a cloth coat and a dark hat, spoke out spontaneously, saying how remarkable it is that children notice these things.

I have never forgotten the texture of this incident. Whenever I recall it I am moved not so much by any sense of my young self but by a sense of responsibility toward children, knowing how acutely I was affected in that moment by that woman's words. The effect, for all I know, has lasted a lifetime.

Now, years later, I live in a rain forest in western Oregon, on the banks of a mountain river in relatively undisturbed country, surrounded by 150-foot-tall Douglas firs, delicate deer-head orchids, and clearings where wild berries grow. White-footed mice and mule deer, mink and coyote move through here. My wife and I do not have children, but children we know, or children whose parents we are close to, are often here. They always want to go into the woods. And I wonder what to tell them.

In the beginning, years ago, I think I said too much. I spoke with an encyclopedic knowledge of the names of plants or the names of birds passing through in season. Gradually I came to say less. After a while the only words I spoke, beyond answering a question or calling attention quickly to the slight difference between a sprig of red cedar and a sprig of incense cedar, were to elucidate single objects.

I remember once finding a fragment of a raccoon's jaw in an alder thicket. I sat down alongside the two children with me and encouraged them to find out who this was — with only the three teeth still intact in a piece of the animals' maxilla to guide them. The teeth told by their shape and placement what this animal ate. By a kind of visual extrapolation its size became clear. There were other clues, immediately present, which told, with what I could add of climate and terrain, how this animal lived, how its broken jaw came to be lying here. Raccoon, they surmised. And tiny tooth marks along the bone's broken edge told of a mouse's hunger for calcium.

We set the jaw back and went on.

If I had known more about raccoons, finer points of osteology, we might have guessed more: say, whether it was male or female. But what we deduced was all we needed. Hours later, the maxilla, lost behind us in the detritus of the forest floor, continued to effervesce. It was tied faintly to all else we spoke of that afternoon.

In speaking with children who might one day take a permanent interest in natural history — as writers, as scientists, as filmmakers, as anthropologists — I have sensed that an extrapolation from a single fragment of the whole is the most invigorating experience I can share with them. I think children know that nearly anyone can learn the names of things; the impression made on them at this level is fleeting. What takes a lifetime to learn, they comprehend, is the existence and substance of myriad relationships: it is these relationships, not the things themselves, that ultimately hold the human imagination.

The brightest children, it has often struck me, are fascinated by metaphor — with what is shown in the set of relationships bearing on the raccoon, for example, to lie quite beyond the raccoon. In the end, you are trying to make clear to them that everything found at the edge of one's senses — the high note of the winter wren, the thick perfume of propolis that drifts downwind from spring willows, the brightness of wood chips scattered by beaver — that all this fits together. The indestructibility of these associations conveys a sense of permanence that nurtures the heart, that cripples one of the most insidious of human anxieties, the one that says, you do not belong here, you are unnecessary.

Whenever I walk with a child, I think how much I have seen

disappear in my own life. What will there be for this person when he is my age? If he senses something ineffable in the landscape, will I know enough to encourage it? — to somehow show him that, yes, when people talk about violent death, spiritual exhilaration, compassion, futility, final causes, they are drawing on forty thousand years of human meditation on this — as we embrace Douglas firs, or stand by a river across whose undulating back we skip stones, or dig out a camas bulb, biting down into a taste so much wilder than last night's potatoes.

The most moving look I ever saw from a child in the woods was on a mud bar by the footprints of a heron. We were on our knees, making handprints beside the footprints. You could feel the creek vibrating in the silt and sand. The sun beat down heavily on our hair. Our shoes were soaking wet. The look said: I did not know until now that I needed someone much older to confirm this, the feeling I have of life here. I can now grow older, knowing it need never be lost.

The quickest door to open in the woods for a child is the one that leads to the smallest room, by knowing the name each thing is called. The door that leads to the cathedral is marked by a hesitancy to speak at all, rather to encourage by example a sharpness of the sense. If one speaks it should only be to say, as well as one can, how wonderfully all this fits together, to indicate what a long, fierce peace can derive from this knowledge.

Healing THE PLANET

HELEN CALDICOTT

The only cure is love. I have just walked around my garden. It is a sunny, fall day, and white fleecy clouds are scudding across a clear, blue sky. The air is fresh and clear with no taint of chemical smells, and the mountains in the distance are ringed by shining silver clouds. I have just picked a pan full of ripe cherry guavas to make jam, and the house is filling with the delicate aroma of simmering guavas. Figs are ripening on the trees and developing that gorgeous deep red glow at the apex of the fruit. Huge orange-coloured lemons hang from the citrus trees, and lettuces, beetroots, and cabbages are growing in the vegetable garden. The fruit and vegetables are organically grown, and it feels wonderful to eat food that is free of manmade chemicals and poisons.

It is clear to me that unless we connect directly with the earth, we will not have the faintest clue why we should save it. We need to have dirt under our fingernails and to experience that deep, aching sense of physical tiredness after a day's labour in the garden to really understand nature. To feel the pulse of life, we need to spend days hiking in forests surrounded by millions of invisible insects and thousands of birds and the wonder of evolution. Of course, I realize that I am very fortunate indeed to be able to experience the fullness of nature so directly — literally in my own backyard. For many people — especially those living in urban areas who are unable to travel out of them regularly — such an experience is difficult to come by. Still, I urge all to try in some way to make a direct connection with the natural world.

Only if we understand the beauty of nature will we love it, and only if we become alerted to learn about the planet's disease processes can we decide to live our lives with a proper sense of ecological responsibility. And finally, only if we love nature, learn about its ills, and live accordingly will we be inspired to participate in needed legislative activities to save the earth. So my prescription for action to save the planet is, Love, learn, live, and legislate.

We must, then, with dedication and commitment, study the harm we humans have imposed upon our beloved earth. But this is not enough. The etiology of the disease processes that beset the earth is a byproduct of the collective human psyche and of the dynamics of society, communities, governments, and corporations that result from the innate human condition.

We have become addicted to our way of life and to our way of thinking. We must drive our cars, use our clothes dryers, smoke our cigarettes, drink our alcohol, earn a profit, look good, behave in a socially acceptable fashion, and never speak out of turn or speak the truth, for fear of rejection.

The problem with addicted people, communities, corporations, or countries is that they tend to lie, cheat, or steal to get their "fix." Corporations are addicted to profit and governments to power, and as Henry Kissinger once said, "Power is the ultimate aphrodisiac."

The only way to break addictive behaviour is to love and cherish something more than your addiction. When a mother and a father look into the eyes of their newborn baby, do they need a glass of beer or a cigarette to make them feel better? When you smell a rose or a gardenia, do you think of work or do you forget for a brief, blissful moment everything but the perfection of the flower? When you see the dogwood flowers hovering like butterflies among the fresh green leaves of spring, do you forget your worries?

Now, try to imagine your life without healthy babies, perfect roses, and dogwoods in spring. It will seem meaningless. We take the perfection of nature for granted, but if we woke up one morning and found all the trees dying, the grass brown, and the temperature 120°F, and if we couldn't venture outside because the sun would cause severe skin burns, we would recognize what we once had but didn't treasure enough to save.

To use a medical analogy: we don't really treasure our good health until we lose it or experience a dreadful accident. When I am injured, I always try immediately after the trauma, psychologically to recapture the moment before, when I was intact and healthy. But it is too late.

It is not too late, though, for our planet. We have ten years of work to do, and we must start now. If we don't, it may be too late for the survival of most species, including possibly, our own.

HEALING THE PLANET

THE BREATHING

Denise Levertov

An absolute
patience.
Trees stand
up to their knees in
fog. The fog
slowly flows
uphill.
White
cobwebs, the grass
leaning where deer
have looked for apples.
The woods
from brook to where
the top of the hill looks
over the fog, send up
not one bird.
So absolute, it is
no other than
happiness itself, a breathing
too quiet to hear.

ACKNOWLEDGMENTS

Every reasonable effort has been made to trace the owners of copyrighted material and to make due acknowledgment. Any errors or omissions drawn to our attention will be gladly rectified in future editions.

"Who Am I?" by Felice Holman, from *At the Top of My Voice and Other Poems*, published by Grosset and Dunlap Inc., A Division of Putnam Publishing Co. © 1970 by Felice Holman.

"The Laws of Nature" by T.C. McLuhan, from *Touch the Earth*. © 1971 by T.C. McLuhan. Reprinted with the permission of Viking Penguin USA.

"Autobiography of a Lungworm" by Roy Fuller. © The Estate of Roy Fuller.

"The Bird and the Snake" by Loren Eiseley. Reprinted with the permission of Atheneum Publishers, an imprint of Macmillan Publishing Company, from *The Firmament of Time* by Loren Eiseley. Copyright © 1960 by Loren Eiseley. Copyright © 1960 by The Trustees of the University of Pennsylvania.

"The Snake" by D.H. Lawrence, from *D.H. Lawrence, Selected Poems*. Copyright © 1923. Copyright © renewed 1951 by Frieda Lawrence. Reprinted with the permission of Viking Penguin USA.

"The Great American Forest" by Rutherford Platt. From the book: *The Great American Forest*. By: Rutherford Platt. © 1965. Used by permission of the publisher: Simon & Schuster Books for Young Readers, New York.

"Walimai" by Isabel Allende. Reprinted with the permission of Atheneum Publishers, an imprint of MacMillan Publishing Company, from *The Stories of Eva Luna* by Isabel Allende, translated from the Spanish by Margaret Sayers Peden. Copyright © 1989 by Isabel Allende. English translation copyright © 1991 by MacMillan Publishing Company.

"The Peace of Wild Things" by Wendell Berry, from *Openings*, copyright © 1968 by Wendell Berry, reprinted by permission of Harcourt Brace Jovanovich, Inc.

"Moss Gathering," copyright 1946 by Editorial Publications, Inc. from *The Collected Poems of Theodore Roethke* by Theodore Roethke. Used by permission of Doubleday, a division of Bantam Doubleday Dell Publishing Group, Inc.

"The House of Life," from *Science Matters: Achieving Scientific Literacy* by Robert M. Hazen and James Trefil. Copyright © 1991 by Robert M. Hazen and James Trefil. Used by permission of Doubleday, a division of Bantam Doubleday Dell Publishing Group, Inc.

"Fable For Tomorrow" by Rachel Carson, from *Silent Spring* by Rachel Carson. Copyright © 1962 by Rachel L. Carson. Copyright © renewed 1990 by Roger Christie. Reprinted by permission of Houghton Mifflin Company. All rights reserved.

"Report on the Earth-Air Addicts" by Robert Priest. Copyright © Robert Priest. All rights reserved. Reprinted from *Scream Blue Living: Poems New and Selected*. The Mercury Press, 1992.

"Still Life" by Ralph Gustafson, from *Landscape with Rain* by Ralph Gustafson. Used by permission of the Canadian Publishers, McClelland & Stewart, Toronto.

"Before Eden" by Arthur C. Clarke. Reprinted by permission of the author and the author's agents, Scott Meredith Literary Agency, Inc., 845 Third Avenue, New York, New York 10022.

"The Scars of Umlungu" by Sindiwe Magona, from *New Internationalist*, April 1992.

"The Wound" from *The General Zapped an Angel* by Howard Fast. Copyright